KERNOW

Ian Gillman

Designed by: Ian Gillman

Photography by: Ian Gillman

Order this book online at www.trafford.com/07-1565
or email orders@trafford.com

Most Trafford titles are also available at major online book retailers.

Note for Librarians: A cataloguing record for this book is available from Library
and Archives Canada at www.collectionscanada.ca/amicus/index-e.html

ISBN: 978-1-4251-3880-6

*We at Trafford believe that it is the responsibility of us all, as both individuals
and corporations, to make choices that are environmentally and socially sound.
You, in turn, are supporting this responsible conduct each time you purchase a
Trafford book, or make use of our publishing services. To find out how you are
helping, please visit www.trafford.com/responsiblepublishing.html*

*Our mission is to efficiently provide the world's finest, most comprehensive
book publishing service, enabling every author to experience success.
To find out how to publish your book, your way, and have it available
worldwide, visit us online at www.trafford.com/10510*

www.trafford.com

North America & international
toll-free: 1 888 232 4444 (USA & Canada)
phone: 250 383 6864 ♦ fax: 250 383 6804
email: info@trafford.com

The United Kingdom & Europe
phone: +44 (0)1865 722 113 ♦ local rate: 0845 230 9601
facsimile: +44 (0)1865 722 868 ♦ email: info.uk@trafford.com

10 9 8 7 6 5 4 3

ACKNOWLEDGEMENTS

The author wishes to thank the library service of Great Britain in general and Northamptonshire libraries in particular for their courtesy, unfailing assistance and interest in this project.

Further, he wishes to thank Janet and Bernard Gillman, Annette Potter and Margaret Morgan for their time in discussions.

The people of Creetown, Kircudbrightshire, and Cornwall, especially around the Truro and Penzance areas.

Thanks to Janet Sheridan for her patience whilst typing from my written text.

Finally, may I dedicate this book to farming people (not forgetting fishing people too) throughout Britain. The independent farming enterprise deserves better from its politicians and bureaucracy, they consistently work very long hours; taking enormous risks due to uncertainties with weather; and having to borrow money to assist cashflow.

Every nation should attempt; as far as it is possible, to produce all of its own staple food requirements.

IAN FRANCIS GILLMAN 2004 – 2006

They have given us into the hand of new unhappy lords,
Lords without anger and honour, who dare not carry their swords.
They fight by shuffling papers; they have bright dead alien eyes;
They look at our labour and laughter as a tired man looks at flies
And the load of their loveless pity is worse than the ancient
wrongs,
Their doors are shut in the evening; and they know no songs.

— G. K. Chesterton, "The Secret People"

INTRODUCTION

The following story is but a novel. However the central characters are based around the actual lives of the maternal grandparents of the author; it shows precisely the very unlikely, improbable even but true, events of their meeting; and subsequent life together.

All other characters are fictional and draw upon the author's extensive travelling.

The twentieth century was the bloodiest one that the world has ever known, with two world wars, evil dictators in abundance, Communism rampant destroying so much in its wake including traditional agricultural practice; National Socialism too advocating its own particular type of terror. British political, economic, judicial, parliamentary and spiritual practice stood out as a beacon of civility in a world seemingly gone mad.

The 1930's depression followed a stock market crash, bringing terrible starvation, bankruptcy and consequential misery.

Farming, with the ongoing production of food and harvesting natural resources is perhaps the most important industry for any country in the world, relying as it does upon sensible political policies. In farming, (horticulture and fishing too), governments and bureaucrats can do so much damage unless they fully understand the needs of the producer and natural world. In Britain for example during two world wars, with naval and submarine blockades, British farming proved its worth keeping a population fed and fit for war.

This story is also a very human one; you will read about so many types of characters and their traits; who made up a formerly very colourful world.

During some very hard times illustrated, love always seemed to find its own way, bringing with it humour, mutual respect and even stoicism. You will hopefully experience those better human traits here along with some unsavoury ones too.

Born in 1952, the author is a countryman who was educated at the Polytechnic of Central London in Regent Street. He was employed by a police force for ten years; taught evening classes for five years and has owned his own business for over twenty years. He rides; particularly enjoying exercising racehorses, plays competitive chess and is a bell ringer.

Upon three occasions he has stood for Parliament, and also other levels of representative government too.

Many of his childhood holidays were spent in Cornwall staying with family members in a beautiful, gentle all-consuming world; now sadly long gone, other than the best of memories of it. The myths, legends and reality of that beautiful county permeate his life, as with this book too.

Well travelled, the author has trudged the pathways of both the ancient and contemporary world observing and absorbing all that he could. He is very concerned about the loss of knowledge and respect for British philosophy.

The author wishes to pay tribute to Herodutus of Halicarnossos and Saul (Paul) of Tarsus, those greatest of characters who walked the highways and byways, leaving for us certain written texts by way of inspiration, regarding the affairs of mankind.

A second book by the author is in preparation, set in Great Helens and Cornwall around 340 B.C.

NB: Recipes for several traditional Cornish dishes are to be found at the end of this book. References to them in the text are marked.

ILLUSTRATIONS

FRONT COVER:
Author's grandfather, (an accomplished horseman and stockman), at Truro School, Cornwall around 1906.
Author's grandmother; a nurse at Nottingham Hospital, around 1914.

BACK COVER
1) Three of the couple's children with lambs on their first farm, around 1927. The author's mother the youngest child, is on the left. The boy in the middle was killed in 1945 piloting a bomber aeroplane and is buried near Jerusalem.
2) Author's mother, around 1927 — who so loved farming life.
3) Harvest, summer 1950. The author's father, left, (about to marry the youngest daughter) lending a hand. Middle — eldest daughter's husband. Right – author's uncle. The all critical harvest drew in the greater family.
4) World War One – train on the Nene Valley Railway, between Peterborough and Stamford. In the First World War men, munitions, and stock were moved by train. Historian Prof. A.J.P. Taylor wrote that the planning and outcome of that war was connected to train timetables. Both livestock and deadstock were usually moved by train.
5) A typical farmyard sight.
6) The author.

CHAPTER I

1958 — Regius Farm, Eatonville, Thurlchester

"This is the BBC Home Service. It is one o'clock on Saturday the fourteenth of November. Here is the news read by Alvar Liddell. Washington has just announced that President Eisenhower will meet with Mr Kruschev early in the New Year, at a location yet to be decided. This follows a lower level meeting between the Soviet Foreign Office, Minister Andri Gromeyko, with his American counterparts in Berlin, yesterday. The Prime Minister, Mr MacMillan, has welcomed the news as a potential thaw in relations between the Soviet Union and the West but has asked that the Sino-Soviet correlation be placed upon the agenda, due to escalating tensions between the two Communist giants, and Peking's antipathy towards India.

"A spokesman for the Prime Minister has announced that Number Ten will send an enhanced delegation of ministers' officials and interested parties to the next European Common Market meeting to be held in Luxembourg in December. It will include trade and industry and defence, together with representatives from agriculture, food and fisheries. The opposition parties declined to offer comment when asked for their opinions regarding this enhanced contact with the former European Coal and Steel Group that is emerging as a unified entity speaking with one voice across the broad range of governmental concerns."

"Edwin, Edwin, Edwin," came the intonation, "Edwin the lunch is ready; have everyone attend the table; the girls are bringing the food in. Exactly where are the other grandchildren?"

Standing at one end of the table Iona untied her apron strings, slipped off the shoulder straps and flicked the garment away, watching it alight upon a chair arm. Turning around to catch a reflected glance of her image within the mirror upon the Welsh Dresser which sat upon a sideboard the farmers wife touched her hair, brushed her chest with her hands as she again faced the table to observe it filling with tureens containing numerous complements to the meat.

The farmer silently cursed the call to the table, instinctively knowing that his news gathering and mental participation in world affairs was over until at least 6 p.m. or perhaps as late as 10 p.m. Perish the thought with such an early start to the milking! However the interests of his head were now overridden by those of his stomach. Further, his genuine gratitude towards his wife, for not just her housekeeping and child-rearing but her farming abilities too, provoked him to therefore attend without further ado.

Trevlyn's interest in world and current affairs had never waned; his table and sitting room were always welcome places for such discussions.

"Dammed rows," Iona always said. Especially so with her sister Fiona around. Fiona was to enjoy a special celebration of her own life upon this occasion but could always be relied upon to argue about politics.

Iona said that arguments distracted from the omnipresent work. That involved cattle, both dairy and steers — those eunuchs of the bovine world. Sheep, pigs and arable farming by way of food production in support of them. In addition, her own extensive poultry enterprise: turkeys both white and bronze, guinea fowl, ducks, geese and chickens. Yes chickens, sold at a day old to smallholders for their part-time enterprises. Certain of the chickens were bred for egg production, others for the table. Chickens that laid eggs for sale and those fattened for the table provided a weekly cash flow.

Never had there been a time, even during the terrible depression of the early 1930s when the family had cried out for food, because of the chickens. Trevelyn always claimed that it was the milk cheque that counted most. Today it was the turn of a bronze turkey to yield itself to Trevelyn's generous table. Chosen for its full and early development, trying the quality of this years stock, a test before the Christmas cull.

Miss Fiona McNiven had just retired as a nurse. Forty-two years nursing including two world wars spent in London, then latterly as a health visitor. She was the only maiden lady in any branch of the family. Combative, well read and travelled, she had witnessed Adolf Hitler speaking at a great 1937 rally in Nuremberg, Germany, and other National Socialist leaders too. Then in the 40s she revisited and saw the result of their ideology. An instinctive disciplinarian, she knew her own mind. Her left wing socialistic tendencies pitted her against the entire family, especially her brother-in-law who, in her words, was a 'Tory farmer'.

That phrase said everything that she wished to convey. However, a lifetime of employment by the state with a guaranteed salary and pension had never endeared her to Edwin, whose forebears had farmed Cornish fields since probably before the Civil War. Nothing in his life or theirs was as certain as a salary or pension.

The vagaries of the elements, the soil and animal health together with personal health had taken its toll upon his psyche. He was not convinced about the worth of many public servants, more especially bureaucrats who in his mind were worthless parasites in a symbiotic relationship with criminals and spivs. His consistently long working day, week, year and milking twice daily, combined with statutory demands for inflated payments of tax, Ministry of Agriculture form-filling, and submission to soft-handed persons with seemingly endless rights causing them not to have to work, jaundiced his opinion and he said sapped his spirit, and certainly that of creative people.

These thoughts notwithstanding, he had changed for lunch; leather boots for brown brogues, a three-piece suit in various shades and flecks of brown: lovatt, moss green and golden hues of autumn. Gone until milking were the breeches: cavalry twill leather leggings with their fifteen buttons each, fastened by a special button hook. The matching worsted jacket and waistcoat too. All that remained was the shirt collar, starched, and attached back and front. His heavy cotton shirt had been replaced with a lighter plain one. As it was a state occasion he had replaced a nondescript tie with a woollen tartan. Very diplomatic; a present from his wife the previous Christmas. Every inch a countryman, at ease with himself, his thoughts, belief systems, indeed the whole philosophy of his life and its raison d'etre. He exuded solidity, gentlemanly decency, and biblical rightness.

Picking up the carving knife, he began to sharpen it, occasionally inspecting its form against the crisp autumn sunlight emanating from a window to his right, then continuing until satisfied with its readiness, a subjective idiosyncrasy.

The clans of three generations had gathered. Blood sons Edward and Charles with their respective families. Edward's wife Ida and three children James, Michael and Charlotte. Theresa, Charles's wife, with Andrew and Rosemary. Daughters Ruth and Heather with husbands Gerard and Francis. Ruth had a daughter, Angela, Heather a son Angus and a daughter Rachel. Nineteen souls would partake in this particular feast.

Iona stood in contemplation, her sister finishing a dry sherry, a grandson Angus was viewing family photographs situated upon a wide window sill. Moving the frames around he was clearly taken by something, but the moment was not yet quite right to formulate a question. Suddenly Great Aunt Fiona clamped her left hand upon his head swivelled it to face her, then spitting upon her small embroidered handkerchief, she applied it to his left cheek area, where apparently filth was lurking. It had never mattered where the boy had encountered this particular species, she could always identify hitherto unknown areas of dirt.

"Boys," she sighed, pushing the object of her matronly attentions away and replacing the handkerchief. Another spit wash had concluded.

"Will you all be seated. Fiona over here please," said Iona. The senior ladies took their places as the turkey began to be dismembered by the newly sharpened knife and plates were moved from the pile to receive their fair share of meat. The two daughters and daughters-in-law were seated, one with baby Charlotte in a high chair, next to her. Their husbands followed, helping daughters to find their places between adults.

Finally the boys; upon these occasions, etiquette established their lowly status in the pecking order. The unwritten code, which Angus thought was designed only to deny him equal access to all of the good things placed before the gathering. Further the indignity of the spit wash still lingered in his conscience. Heather, his mother, had quietly whispered to her son to remember that a generation ago she had been subject to similar treatment, and to forget the incident. Iona dispatched her daughter Ruth to fetch some missing sauce from the lower Aga oven.

The telephone rang; son-in-law Gerard left the dining room to answer it. The noise of knives, spoons, glasses, tureen lids and a dozen conversations gradually rose in decibels. Plates were now full, the gravy and condiments were being passed around. Gerard returned from the kitchen telephone and pushed a piece of folded paper towards his mother-in-law. Flicking it open, she allowed a smile. It was an order. "Two New York dressed chickens, four dozen chicken eggs, and two ducks eggs. Mrs Simmel, Friday!" Holding her smile Iona raised a glass of what she called 'Lions drink', water in fact, and implored everyone to raise their glasses too in order to toast her sister.

"Fiona, happy days in retirement, good health and good luck my dear," to which everyone agreed. Rosemary was heard to ask "What is retirement mummy?" A quick explanation by her parent appeared to suffice.

Conversation gradually increased to in-house jokes, reminders of past misdeeds, failures, forgetfulness, and the range of anecdotes that make family life embarrassing, teasing, annoying, yet compelling. Laughter and a range of human exclamations rent the air as the food was consumed.

The second course was an option of a fruit salad or apple crumble. A family recipe[1] passed from mother to daughter, and indeed across families, especially when a daughter-in-law enjoyed closeness to her husband's mother. The more substantial pudding was for the particular benefit of Trevelyn and his eldest son Edward, who bore the brunt of the physical demands of the farm, which were considerable. Others partook of the crumble but in a lesser quantity.

Great Aunt Fiona suddenly, and almost without explanation or provocation, alighted upon Heather. "Your boy, my dear is becoming far too Americanised, now I understand that Mr. and Mrs. Woods have given him a so-called 'steam radio'. May I suggest that he tunes it in to Mr. Alistair Cooke, whose broadcast from America will redress his overoptimistic view of that particular republic."

A discussion concerning the precise subjects covered by Mr. Cooke during his 'Letter from America' broadcast ran on for a while. She went on to allude that all cowboys had lice, rickets and other unmentionable diseases.

Yet still the boy was undimmed by his fascination. He had asked for a cowboy kit for Christmas with twin Derringer guns. Surely his Pye Invictor radio would not quench that aspiration? It was giving him access to the globe through the British Broadcasting Corporation's World Service, with broadcasts from even secretive Moscow by Eric De Morney. There were superb comedies such as 'The Goon Show' with Peter Sellers and Spike Milligan, the funniest men upon the planet, and Jimmy Clitheroe whose treatment of his long suffering sister Susan replicated that by many a brother. 'The Navy Lark' too, perhaps reflected albeit in jest some experiences of older male relatives performing either their National Service or Regular Service. It provided an irreverent look at life within that particular Armed Service. 'Test Match Special' commenting upon the cricket; 'Desert Island Discs' choosing your favourite eight pieces of music; then the American Forces radio stations bringing jazz, especially 'BeBop', Miles Davis, John Coltrane and Stan Getz, and the incredible piano sounds of Dave Brubeck too. The blues, then its derivative rhythm and blues; played by musicians who had taken the railroad from New Orleans and The Delta county up to Chicago and the northern industrial cities, recordings of which were so difficult and expensive to obtain in grey war-ravished Britain of the 1950s. Especially so, as pocket money was not too plentiful.

The conversation had inevitably turned to the farm, as family gatherings at the seat of the family wealth do. Trevelyn was again feeling the pressure from his Cornish family to return to the duchy. The summer visits had always been difficult, especially during his father's life. Crossing the Tamar River in 1914 for war was one thing but having survived, returned and re-crossed it was another issue entirely.

Before his death and the Second World War, Edward had spoken words that still resonated, from the Book of Numbers, Verse 34. 'This shall be your land with its boundaries all around.' Moses was invoked to pull his son closer to Cornish soil. A very devout man of strong principles and rigid discipline, who had used large sums of his own money to assist in building a chapel and other similar projects, it was beyond his thinking that a man born and bred west of the River Tamar in Cornubia – 'land of the saints' would ever find a reason for spending long on the eastern side. That was another place, referred to sometimes dismissively, even contemptuously as 'upcountry'.

Oh how persuasive the Celtic pull was, but why? Pressure exerted for the return to Cornwall was evenly applied to all generations. It was verbal, written in letters and commemorative cards, whispered even. A divine request delivered almost involuntarily from a being with intuitive preservationist instincts.

Sitting at the head of his table in Regius Farm Eatonville, one and a half miles outside the small cathedral city of Thurlchester, his roots in his own soil were deep enough he thought. Viewing his wife across the table, their surviving two sons, two daughters, four in-laws, and eight grandchildren, hearing the wondrous sounds emanating from the assembled throng should have been sufficient. The harvest was in, farm and family were secure for another year. Christmas and New Year would pass in relaxation before the hard work of the winter: milking twice daily in poor weather, hedging, ditching and all of the preparatory work before the spring planting and sowing.

The meal and conversation emanating had concluded. Fiona was drawn into the sitting room. Iona remained in the dining room polishing the silver pieces and putting away various items. The four girls organised the washing up to keep Iona out of the scullery. They giggled together, then shared serious conversation interspersed with ribald comments!

It was the four o'clock milking that broke up the gathering as Edwin and son Edward went to change. The farmer left the house flipping on his trademark bowler hat, which was only removed whilst milking when it hung upon a peg, exchanged for a flat cap. The cap was greasy on the top; it had pushed against the flanks of cows thousands of times as the beasts were manoeuvred into place for the milking machine. With his head balanced against the cow, the farmer took hold of a teat, cleaned it with a rag and water then squeezed out a drop of milk to cleanse the duct, prior to attaching the milking device.

Then the farm cats would line up by the udder, open their mouths wide squinting their eyes to receive the squirts of milk into their open gullets. Droplets would then be meticulously licked and pawed off their faces, whiskers and anywhere a splash occurred. This ritual was repeated until milking was complete, when the cattle would be returned to the pastures from whence they had been taken, as the cats again disappeared to secret places that only felines seem to know of.

Many flies arrived during the milking procedure; in response the cows simultaneously ruminated and defecated while continually swishing their tails to dislodge the interlopers, flitting off the objects causing annoyance sometimes into the windows where, ensnared by cobwebs they were watched then devoured by spiders, who lurked within stone crevasses or the gap between sill and window frame. Nature determined the chance of a meal for all who turned up to feast in so many circumstances.

Upon completion of milking they removed the liquid to a nearby building known as the 'milk parlour' where the product was cooled then placed into churns which the men transported to the farm gate for collection by the dairy in Thurlchester; who were now required by statute to pasteurize all milk. Finally it would be bottled and sealed pending delivery to household doorsteps; perhaps in conjunction with other fresh and nourishing farm produce.

Meanwhile within the farmhouse the family were destined for the tea table or failing a heavy lunch, as upon this occasion the dinner table. The two men returned to the celebration and tea, which would be soon interrupted due to the younger generation's requirement for sleep. Edwin challenged his sister-in-law to play draughts, a popular evening pursuit. The winners then played Iona, and so forth. He teased the women that it was training for the winter leagues!

During a break from playing, Edwin lit his pipe, and drawing upon its stem, puffing exotic aromas into the sitting room, stared long and hard into the open crackling fire. At one point he stood, drew back a curtain to look across the garden up towards a meadow.

A cat known as Nimrod suddenly appeared upon the window sill, glared at him and howled, evidently wanting to enter the house, yet all of the time knowing that it was strictly forbidden territory for cats. As his name implied he was of a warrior class: the hunting and shooting variety. Staring out of the window and into the gloom the farmer gave thought to his family, Cornwall, and his ancestors back over the generations. Farming was his life, their life, but he felt trapped, and guilty for leaving what they regarded as 'God's country', 'hallowed turf'.

His thoughts went as deep as Anicius Boethuis in his 'Consolation of Philosophy'. A volume that was for a thousand years second only to the Holy Bible in popularity. Was he too permanently condemned by his own decisions and actions? Why was he tormented by the pull of Kernow? His natural radical eloquence flowed through his mind. Perhaps life 'upcountry' had debased his philosophy and that of his kin. His father and so much that he had preached now resonated. He could accept condemnation for leaving Cornwall because there would never be execution, in a physical sense, for his actions. Unlike Boethius in 520 A.D. Having served his country well, and its ideology, his mental imprisonment was confusing.

Plenty, and her well stocked horn, Cornucopia, had not been entirely his; the struggle of farming saw to that. "No man is rich who shakes and groans convinced that he needs more," was a quotation that he was unable to recall the source of. Yet he was philanthropic; known to be generous and had never been a greedy man. Unlike so many so-called businessmen in the city of Thurlchester he was not incarcerated within in a prison of materialism, yet could not understand what was missing. Perhaps it was just a moment with his own personal time-clock; older age brings with it more philosophical thought.

Then he heard the voice of Angus, asking his grandmother about the family photographs upon the sideboard in the dining room; he had begun to question family history and the past, particularly since his own brush with mortality. The boy had developed chronic bronchitis each winter, hay fever during spring and summer then managed to acquire every illness known, from whooping cough to scarlet fever, mumps to chicken pox; but it was a particular virulent measles strain on top of the winter chronic bronchitis that very nearly finished him.

Choosing more mellow pastimes then, he had taken to chess, including a postal competition using a printed postcard bought from good stationers or the Post Office, with a chess board printed thereon for marking; thus communicating his next move to an opponent somewhere in the world. Thereby a stamp collection was born, out of postal chess.

Fishing too was his hobby, especially for Perch, and the wily Pike who hid within reeds; all whilst listening to a newly available miniaturized transistor radio thus maintaining contact with cricket test matches courtesy of Mr. John Arlott. Music was dominant however: piano and organ. Always busy, never experiencing boredom or loneliness — those afflictions that affect so many — continually doing something, creating in some way, whilst fighting the demons of illness that only by the intake of penicillin with streptomycin in copious quantities did victory emerge; just, from a seemingly hopeless situation.

Grandson Angus questioned who, what, why, when, or if. He travelled well, determined in his pursuit of knowledge, and now quizzed his grandparents doggedly. Why did some of the men in the family photographs wear skirts? Have the family always worked Regius Farm? Who was who in the zoo? A river appearing within a photograph did not appear familiar; where was it? Questions followed questions. He needed to know about his origins.

The summer holidays in Cornwall had provided enormous pleasure and much adventure. On Great Uncle Provin's farm he had ridden his first horse. The farmer had always kept three horses, in different stages of life and development. A terrifying initiation, trotting and cantering around an exercise paddock, eliciting the comment: 'He is a horseman.' Uncle Provin roared with laughter. The boy only knew that he was alive!

At Perranporth the caves, then chapel rock with its natural pool, sand dunes to dig holes as far as Australia, cream teas, old tin mines, looking for adders, (the only poisonous snake in Britain), creating plays and entertainment for adults with older cousins, and the sheer excitement of Camelot. The exploration encompassed the myths of King Arthur and reality of Land's End. 'The Lizard' with its serpentine rock, Marazion; the beautiful village opposite St Michael's Mount; St Mawes and Falmouth with their boats; the north Cornwall coast of Zennor with tales of shipwreck booty and smugglers; did not John Meade Faulkner articulate similar excitement within his book 'Moonfleet'? At Tintagel and Boscastle there were cliffs of unrivalled danger and excitement to scale, whilst being watched by a variety of noisy seabirds whose squawk was only drowned by the crash of another pounding wave, as they have done since before even the saints trod this land as their own.

There was so much adventure for a boy that he needed many return summer visits in order to enjoy it all, then many family requests to return forever. Why did he not live in Cornwall, he persisted, when most of the family said he should? Why did the Cornish family not wear skirts? The questions were endless.

The boy's grandfather began talking to him, explaining how in fact he actually did not hail from Thurlchester but had bought a farm in the area following his marriage. Then the move to their present farm, which offered greater scope for development. Originally their home was named Assers Farm. Regius Farm was built around 1509, the very year when Henry — the first Tudor monarch — having won his crown on Bosworth field from the last Plantagenet, yielded not to a sword, but to his maker. The earlier act of regicide in Leicestershire in 1485 had ushered in a period of caution and thrift. Clever propaganda by the new ruling family and a playwright called Mr. William Shakespeare ensured that their immediate predecessor was painted in rather a poor light. The new monarch had sought peace, security and trade, successfully filling his administrations coffers. Such was the confidence in the country that by his natural demise, the unexpected accession by his second son Henry — the firstborn Arthur having sadly died prematurely — caused little concern for the political and diplomatic process, or the economy.

Subsequently the farm, as with many others, saw an expansion, with a two-storey barn added to the western end, which would eventually become part of the main house. The land was easy to cultivate, a fine tilth could be achieved; it drained naturally into Assers Brook which transported excess rainfall down to the River Kells. Gently rolling, undulating contours allowing human and animal alike easy access during every season.

Thomas Wolsey, during his rapid ascendancy, had acquired much of the better land and farms in and around the area. Farms and their income complemented his several houses. Local administration of the then tenanted farms was in the city just one and a half miles away. Overall jurisdiction was however carried on from London, where decisions were made for local implementation. Wolsey renamed the property Cardinal Farm, planted a walnut tree in the front garden and decreed that upon the day following the livestock and general produce market in Thurlchester he wished for prayers to be said prior to national and local news being read by the incumbent clergy of the village to the laity, from around and eventually beneath the tree. This in fact continued until the village school had been built during the late nineteenth century. At the time of the inception of the idea, there being few literate villagers other than clergymen, larger farmers and aristocracy who owned land nearby, it was deemed a service by the church to keep the general population informed regarding all matters of general concern.

The income from the farm was paid to Cardinal College Oxford, which was founded by Wolsey. For displeasing his monarch the Cardinal was initially charged with high treason, then 'praemunire' — an offense against the English crown punishable by forfeiture of land — in 1529. Despite being the King's chief advisor, he met the axe and block in 1530. Following his death, and the subsequent break with Rome, the Act of Supremacy in 1534 and abolishment of payments of first harvests (or annates) to the Pope in Rome there was not only a change to the Book of Common Prayer that was used for religious practice around the farm's walnut tree; changes to the lower rituals and symbolism of Protestantism were employed thereafter. The farm was then subjected to another significant change in circumstance.

The Crown took possession of Wolsey's freeholds. Various properties and holdings were sold off by the King, in order to finance the former Cardinal College, renamed Christ Church College, in Oxford. Henry renamed the holding Regius Farm, thus hopefully expunging the memory of Wolsey, who had in his mind failed him.

Reluctantly the entire village was sold off by the Crown. By reducing his outgoings around Thurlchester the King was able to underwrite Christ Church College. With Thurlchester losing its abbey and collegiate status in 1535 to the ongoing reformation, its magnificent cathedral and precincts dedicated to St Oswold being relegated, authority drained away, then, even more so during the rise of nonconformist religious practices during the following two centuries.

So it was that a monotheistic doctrine eventually split, giving rise to quite different approaches regarding teaching, architecture and lifestyles. The practical significance of this evolution as opposed to revolution being that despite a civil war later, there was never to be a true revolution by comparison say with the French; (indeed sadly just too many continental European countries who found a need to cull one another) — but a 'Glorious Revolution' — that uniquely British phenomenon.

All of the time though the laity were gradually encouraged to themselves actually participate in religious service, sacrament ritual and ongoing understanding of the Biblical word, as opposed to just receiving it from their 'betters, combined with ever greater national suffrage, press and publishing freedoms, labour unions, sporting inventions various parliamentary reform acts, a certain amount of social mobility assisted in preventing the all-pervading strife prevalent in Europe and elsewhere. Combined, these developments were an essential precursor to breeding and nurturing a more relaxed population, which assisted an amazing intellectual outpouring in literature, invention, arts, exploration, innovation, architecture, and ideas of political, economic, judicial, parliamentary and spiritual practice. After Great Helens, Great Britain. Then perhaps, nothing; dust to dust?

This situation encouraged investment in farming and its associated practices, which naturally developed in sophistication thus keeping the British nation mostly fed, that is by comparison with other nations of any given era.

Regius Farm passed through generations of various families, or their branches, firstly due to primogeniture, (the right of the first-born to inherit), then its failure due to unproductive breeding, human failings such as bankruptcy, drunkenness and other tomfoolery. Occasionally nature intervened with repeatedly bad weather at the wrong moment. Such inconsistency of pattern causing the all crucial harvest to fail. "The valleys are so thick with corn that even they are singing," is a choral anthem often sung in church at harvest festival; it was tragically sometimes an anthem of wishful thinking.

Whereas death perhaps stalked some, thus tragically 'The Lamentations of Jeremiah the Prophet' expressed by the Tudor composer Thomas Tallis, with a vocal cry singing such lines as: "Spare O Lord, your people, spare them. Do not consign your children to destruction," would often have been more apposite. Or even 'The Dream of Gerontius' depicting the moments of passing from life through to death, composed by Edward Elgar, using words by the famous Cardinal Newman, was perhaps sadly more apt sometimes at the autumn festival as yet another family slaughtered then ate their remaining stock and loaded up their carts, taking such transferable worldly possessions as could be mustered; prior to a moneylender sealing the property pending its sale; perhaps to his friend or relation with a different surname.

The liquidated and auctioned farm was merely everyday swag to the banker, perhaps an opportunity to grasp a freehold, sometimes even because of fickle and obstinate politics changing a policy, thus destroying a market. The banal, genial affability of the moneylender was all too easily mistaken as courtesy though it was certainly commensurate with flaws and weakness of character; of low moral fibre. Debt, with its social shame and personal humiliation, was other people's problem.

Such are the vagaries of agriculture and occasional sadness of Michaelmas. The Trevelyn family had avoided that. Sometimes however, only just.

Trevelyn did actually take risks to indicate that he was independent in mind and practice of thought. He lived by his own wits, intuition and knowledge acquired from not only teachers but experience. Few men dared to stand alone, and by their own risk-taking. Yet this one did. As he gazed out of the window drawing on his pipe, the swirling drifting smoke reflected his mind at that moment...

CHAPTER II

1914 — Chyancelt Farm, Truro, Cornwall

The atmosphere and bustle at Chyancelt Farm upon this particular day was similar to the preparations in many homes during the morning just prior to a family wedding ceremony; when all of those present find something to panic about. The kitchen was humming with activity everybody with something to say, fewer willing to listen though.

Edwin's three sisters: Martha, Charlotte and Agnes, were busily folding his clothes, preparing food and packing items for his imminent journey by horse. A volunteer into the Cornish Yeomanry, the twenty-four-year-old farmer, a typical bright-eyed open character with a sharp mind, defied his father and enlisted. Conscription may well have occurred but that did not help his father with seven days a week milking and all of the other stock to tend.

Meanwhile the housekeeper Mary Lee was occasionally tending a large cauldron of hare shackles [2] upon the kitchen range while ironing and listening to the nervous talk concerning the likely destiny of Edwin. A tortoiseshell cat had stolen into forbidden territory, perhaps encouraged by cooking aromas, settling under the table, out of sight and reach, busy with its own cleansing routine. Its movements were similar to those of a cellist!

Outside the daily work of the farm progressed at its usual pace. Milking had Finished; Edward Trevelyn's magnificent herd of one hundred and fifteen Channel Island cattle, with a few Pembrokeshire, Montgomeryshire and Glamorgan cows, had returned to their current pastures. Churns containing the milk were transported by horse and cart from the milking parlour, the half mile on the farm driveway around the St Guren Oak on the ridge in the land, and down to the Falmouth Road, where they were placed by the granite gate posts onto a wooden plinth in preparation for the dairy collection lorry en route to Truro. Some milk was retained for later sale to nearby houses and for the farmhouse consumption, including clotted cream and cheese-making.

Pigs were being mucked out and grumbling until placated with autumn windfall apples. Their scoffing appeared to produce an inane smile upon their faces as they dribbled saliva mixed with apple juice everywhere, grunting until the next precious fruit was spied. The horses had already been groomed and turned out into the fields for the day from their overnight stables, except Edwin's which was yet to transport him away. The odd hen passed by looking for additions to the early feed. Elsewhere ongoing maintenance was a continuing necessity to buildings and machinery alike. Fields were being tended; preparations for the next round of milking were always required.

Trevelyn Senior returned to the house for the lunch with his three daughters and son. The housekeeper was invited to dine with them; she had been a servant upon the farm since the death of his second wife during childbirth. Losing two wives this way was sufficient to cool his ardour, causing him to settle for the family already conceived with his first love Ruth, and devote time and energy to the Lord's work.

So it was that six adults sat down in the formal dining room, broke homemade brown bread together, ate bowls of shackled hare – a dish of leftover meat, bones and stock together with different vegetables all simmered together. A very rich concoction. Followed by fresh fruit, homemade sour cheese and biscuits. Conversation of a tense nature was interspersed with fun yet nervousness.

However Edwin was elated, ready for a fight. His odyssey to draw upon Homer and ancient Greek literature was about to begin. Would there be a Helen for him? Or was the beautiful daughter of King Tyanderos of Sparta purely a myth? Surely she was euphuism for every brave young blade's inspiration. After all 'Faint hearts never win fair maiden' and he was not faint-hearted.

Perhaps he would suit a 'Penelope' who was wise and faithful; or were his thoughts merely a simile for a Maud, Cicily or an Ethel? Help! Whoever, whatever, as long as it was fun.

He was about to ride out on Buceuphalus, well Morvah actually. His mount meant no less to him than Alexander's and surely they would return together, Morvah and Edwin; unlike the Macedonian and his mount Buceuphalus.

The Cornish Yeomanry had an aura of 'gung ho' and a reputation that nothing, no known discipline could secure their minds. Actions therefore followed. No 'lotus-eaters' these. Brave to a man, certain of their mission, true iconoclasts when faced with the image of the military superiority of an enemy. Especially Continental European ones, whose people were treated as little more than cattle or even non-ruminant mammals. The European swine were once again to be taught a proper lesson. Napoleon who? Democracy, truly only accepted by Great Britain from Great Helens would prevail if necessary from the end of a bayonet. Were Herodotus still writing 'The Histories' this episode would be worthy of Book Ten, surely.

So a young man bade farewell to all that. Secured tack to Morvah his mount; strapped his rucksack of belongings carefully prepared upon his back and in a very shy way kissed three sisters farewell; shook the hand of the housekeeper and finally that of his father. Mary Lee moved forward, handing the future yeoman soldier a package wrapped in greaseproof paper containing a Cornish pasty [3], which she had made that morning using the proper traditional Cornish recipe. Although Trevelyn would not be able to eat it in the usual way, with milk, nevertheless he would enjoy chewing it en-route.

Agnes, shortly to be married and moving to the Penzance area to commence married life and farming, looked longingly at her only brother. The uncertainties of her future written all over her face reflected his future too. Charlotte, the extrovert, wholly confident upon any stage, determined, indefatigable, awaiting only success, grabbed her brother hugged and held him saying, "Au revoir until, well next time." (She had a spirited phrase for every situation.) Then Martha, the real talent of the girls, her future certain, moved forward to touch her brother's shoulder. Already several times the Cornish Champion of Dressage, representing her beloved county at national level, she mounted her own horse in readiness to accompany her brother off the property.

Eyes were caught, looks passed, a very British way of expressing emotions: much said, but little spoken. The remaining group and staff stood on the edge of the farmyard watched and waved as Martha led her brother up the slow incline, a quarter of a mile to the ridge and the giant old oak tree named after St Guren. Anecdotal evidence suggested that prayer meetings had occurred around the site of the oak and that a well had existed there, thus creating a natural meeting point.

As they reached the summit they turned their horses around to face back from whence they came. They viewed the River Fal and Truro River; the familiar granite farm and buildings, with external steps up to the first floor lofts, around the yard they glanced as in the distance Charlotte began jumping up and down, waving and shouting.

On they rode down the driveway, the second quarter of a mile to the entrance gate, the metal grating and milk plinth, where empty churns now sat. They paused; Martha rode alongside her brother leaned sideways towards him kissing his cheek.

They looked hard at each other and she said, "Now my boy make sure you return in one piece, father cannot run this farm without you and he has plans to buy more land on the Gloweth side remember."

Edwin laughed, "Of course I will return, they say it will be over by Christmas anyway, it's just a little fun, gets me away from milking and the chapel people."

"Furthermore," said Martha now wagging her finger. "Do not, do you hear me, do not bring any foreign woman home. Father has eyes on young Molly Polwithel for you."

"Never!" barked Edwin. "She has a bent nose and is growing a moustache."

"Stop it," retorted his sister. "Anyway there are several more at chapel, and other women attending Kenwyn Church, and that is without looking outside Truro."

"We will see," said Edwin.

"Yes we will see. Now be off with you," finished Martha. They both smiled.

Edwin leaned over to a gate attached to a granite post by the cattle grating, lifted up a stay, manoeuvred his horse around the gate, dropped the stay back over the granite post retook his reins with both hands, smiled and laughed at Martha calling, "Now no girls with a moustache remember!" They both waved. He turned and rode on soon arriving at the Falmouth Road horse and rider curved eastwards. Soon within the city limits he passed on the left his sister's old school, then at the junction of Daniel Street and Infirmary Hill he glanced at The Jolly Tinners Public House. Should he stop, have a friendly drink and tell the regulars where he was going? No better not, word would inevitably reach his teetotal father and provoke trouble.

A cottage nearby had the door open, despite the season; an old woman sat at the threshold sucking upon a rag, gurgling and generally abusing the world. The rag was impregnated with Madame Genieva's 'Mother's ruin' — better known as gin. When she pulled the rag away, to utter nonsensical words, her mouth showed peg teeth of black and green. It looked foul in there and probably stunk, thought Edwin.

On he went, walking down the very steep Lemon Street with its beautiful Georgian terraces, over the River Kenwyn, into Boscawen Street, whose mansions did not belie their past. The Philharmonic Society held its winter season balls there: a cultural and intellectual atmosphere developed by the Royal Institution of Cornwall because London was far away and communications were poor. Then, right to the Coinage Hall.

A public telephone area by the hall was the designated army rendezvous point. The horse could not walk upon the cobbled streets and therefore had to use the pavement, An army sergeant from the barracks in Bodmin, Trevelyn's first overnight destination had instructed him to meet with other recruits at 1400 hours, by the telephone kiosks outside the hall, then when all were assembled they were to telephone the barracks for more information.

Presently the other two recruits arrived, one from Shortlanesend, the other from Tresillian. Both farmer's sons brought up with horses; they were very comfortable in the saddle. Both however younger than Edwin. They introduced themselves. All were aware of who the others were and where their families farmed. Cornwall being Cornwall it was impossible to hide. The telephone call to Bodmin barracks told them that transport would not be calling at Truro, it was collecting at Newquay and would meet them at 1630 in Indian Queens by the junction of the Penzance and Newquay roads.

"Then we had better trot on," said one.

"Check your girths first," said another and they lifted first one leg then the other pulling the girth straps where necessary and pushing the pin into a tighter hole. When attaching tack onto horses; sometimes they have fun by blowing out their stomachs, causing the girth to remain slack. Potentially the saddle can slide around and the rider tips off. They wanted to ride along Princes Street to the quay and out, but commercial activity prevented this, so the longer route around the hall was necessary.

The Coinage Hall was one of four taxation halls in Cornwall for the Stannaries, the mining administration areas of the county. Truro was a coinage town for the Tywarnhaile area. The Duchy of Cornwall took tax on all tin mined. The hall was close to the confluence of the rivers Allen and Kenwyn; where they became the Truro River the quay and harbour were there. So it was that they crossed the River Allen by Newbridge Street, bore right then left into Tregolls Road and prepared to leave their city.

Edwin quickly looked right to Trennick Lane, glanced up to the conglomeration of buildings that constituted Truro School and addressing the school said, "Why did you insist on Latin and Greek, when I wanted engineering drawing and biology? I fully understood your English and mathematics, but horsemen do not need art. Sorry if I caused you any annoyance, but thank you."

They rode out of the city towards St Erme and Trispen. At the top of the hill they glanced back at their Celtic capital, the three towers of the cathedral dedicated to St Mary were majestic. A Great Western train was smoking its way over the many arches of the bridge and into the station. Gradually a glance westwards did not show Truro behind them.

The conversation left their shared inheritance, moving on to the unfurling European adventure. What would the food be like? Would they drink wine? The Continentals did, with their meals too! Girls; how would they communicate with the local girls? It all seemed so glamorous. A collective sense of patriotic undertaking gave way to a hymn being sung: 'Jerusalem'. "And did those feet in ancient times..." The singing lasted for a while as the trot continued. There were periods of story telling, joking and silence. A few people to acknowledge, horses and wagons travelling either way and sometimes children waved and stared. Tennyson's poem 'Maud' was chanted

"Singing of men that in battle away.
Ready in heart and ready in hand.
March with banner, and bugle and fife.
To the death, for their native land."

One traveller remarked that the ancient Greeks drank wine made from dates when attacking the Persian empire. "How exotic," said another. Then they sang "Ride on, ride on, in majesty. Hark, all the tribes Hosanna cry." Another stirring tune from the remembered hymnal fell readily from their lips: "Onward Christian soldiers, marching as to war, forward into battle, see his banners go." Then later: "We are not divided all one body we, one in hope and doctrine and one in charity."

As the conversation moved on to the coming fight, they quite naturally produced a rendering of "Fight the good fight with all thy might." All very healthy outpourings of a homogenous people rising up as a united body to quell the barbarians.

They made good time, arriving early at Indian Queens but were preceded by two army wagons for horse transport. A corporal was to give them their first experience of army life by screeching, "You're late! The sergeant will have your guts for garters!"

"Actually we are early," said the youngest lad.

"What?" boomed the corporal. "Do not argue with me. Load your horses into the box. I want to eat tonight. Those first in the queue get the best platefuls and a chance of seconds if they are quick."

"Do you serve French wine Sir?" said one.

The corporal just stared, wide-eyed and open-mouthed. The experienced horsemen loaded their mounts into the boxes which had a cake of hay inside for each animal. The corporal drove one wagon; a driver the other one. There were now eight horses and the future Cornish Yeomanry moving eastwards slowly towards Bodmin where avoiding the tricky right hand turn by the Shire Hall they turned left in Bore Street for Dennison Road passing the once all powerful St Petroc's Church, the largest parish church in the county. The distinctive squat tower less of a landmark since the terrible storm and lightning of 1699, when 150 feet of spire obeyed the laws of gravity.

The army wagons were obeying the laws of their drivers' stomachs as they selected a low gear and put their feet hard down on the accelerator to climb up Priory Road to the barracks. A rather grim building with its souvenir cannon from the Napoleonic wars of 100 years previously loomed.

"Anyway," said someone, "Who was Napoleon? We stored him in the man of war 'Bellerophon' as a captive, near Cawsand in Cornwall before sending him to Elba in exile. So as for the Kaiser and his lot, bring them on."

"Yeah the Kaiser would not dare visit Cornwall," said another. Similar bellicose comments were passed which bolstered morale, gave common cause, helped make merry. Through the central archway they drove, onto the square and the stables.

"All out, horses tended before men," was the first order. They fed and watered the animals then pledged to revisit them before bed. Inside an open coal and wood fire awaited, the card table, draughts and chess too, but first, to be shown their quarters, eat, then clear up.

They were provided with a hearty meal and the new volunteers from around Cornwall were required to assist with clearing up. Young farming men were not used to domestic work: theirs was a world of horses and machines, farm animals and fields; inside was for the staff, mothers and sisters depending upon economic circumstance. Further, the social constraints prevented them from acquiring such knowledge; they were not welcome in the scullery where decisions were taken that they could never be a part of. After all, they were men.

Everyone ate well, an instant rapport developed as those who were to be 'la crème de la crème' of the Cornish Yeomanry asserted their superiority and were slapped down by the serving regulars present! After supper was cleared away to the satisfaction of the sergeant, he instructed the corporal to return to the stables and supervise all men with horses, which was quickly accomplished. One was told to carry out a final check before bed. The men returned to the sitting room, a fire was stoked. 'Sparks' – known as soldiers and sailors traced a patten; moving, seemingly running over and around deposits of soot upon the back firebrick.Cigarettes were lit by some a couple of older men used pipes;. A compendium of games appeared containing halma, draughts, ludo, several packs of greasy playing cards, snakes and ladders and a horse race game using dice. Elsewhere a chess set lay beneath several daily newspapers. Everyone found a pastime.

One introverted type played Patience with cards away from the crowd; perhaps missing his family or just contemplating the unknown. Uncertainties affect people in different ways. It is usual that the one with lots to say, the empty verbage, braggadocio of the salesman type, will run and hide first, or faint like a soppy girl with vapours. The stoic, is nearly always reliable, intense perhaps, fails to communicate because of a deeper thought yes, but will actually perform without fuss when required, and not spend the next year boasting about it; adding ever more embellishments at another bar with a new audience.

Around 2215 the sergeant appeared and requested the corporal do a last check upon the horses; that duty performed lights out were at 2245. The fire guard was suitably placed. Reveille was at 0630. They were to remain in Bodmin the following day and night, then leave by train the day after that.

During the following day all of the new recruits and volunteers were entered into the Attestation Book, a record of men as they enlist. The Royal 1st Devon Yeomanry; Cornish Yeoman Squadrons; the various platoons being drawn from the larger towns of the county. (The Devon Yeomanry were called up on the 4th of August 1914; the regulars rushed to the east coast to guard against an invasion that never came. The initial concern regarding invasion gave way; the regulars and territorials were soon busily engaged in necessary preparation.)

Then, a medical. Every recruit was subjected to a full medical. Typically ; many of the popular 'in' jokes and memorable anecdotes that could be shared were exchanged during this process. Morale was usually lifted by participating in humour.

After various other administration matters the group now assembled were to journey to the Isle of Wight for initial training for four months, at the end of which a leave of two weeks would be taken, before the roster for postings was revealed.

Quite what was in store was as yet unknown, but exciting nevertheless. These characters were not 'lotus eaters', (the plant represented in Greek legend as inducing dreaminess together with a luxurious lifestyle and indolence); the Libyan coast from where the plant was allegedly obtained had no allure. The Emperor Napoleon Bonaparte had been vanquished and these Cornishmen's forebears returned home in triumph. The Kaiser was just another European dictator whose people were citizens of his state; he was not a servant of the people; but as with old Europe, contemptuous of our British common law rights; our civil lives away from state control, their ruling class was their state, and vice versa. The Cornish Yeomanry would defend free speech, Parliamentary democracy, the elected person over the unelected commissar. So the die was cast from a reliable mould.

Trevelyn's group caught the train from Bodmin. It stopped at Liskeard for an hour whilst more troops boarded, then onto Plymouth where linking with others from around Devon they formed a cohesive group that would subsequently board a ship in The Solent. From Plymouth the train journeyed to Exeter, via Bridport, Dorchester , Christchurch and Lymington. Then, by ferry to Yarmouth. The Solent had mercifully been calm for the crossing. However the army logistics covered every possibility; care of rider and mount seemingly effortless for this the finest institution of its type in the world.

The Cornish, Devon and Dorset men were now safely ensconced for a period of twenty weeks. The senior regiment in Great Britain, Royal 1st Devon Yeomanry were now camped around Parkhurst Forest. The Cornish squadrons being tented with one another. During the four months they would undergo numerous training activities, from drill, cross-country running, gymnasium work, firearms training, personal care and horsemanship. Edwin was very fit, used to camping for pleasure alongside the Carrick roads around Mylor, Feock, Kea, even up as far as Tresillian.

There was little that he did not know about horses but just needed to have his existing knowledge honed to British Army requirements. Parkurst Forest and Brightstone Down would provide the testing grounds for both man and horse. So it was for what seemed four very short months. Christmas came and went; two days leave was insufficient to return home. The farm was now connected to the Post Office telephone system: Truro 9. A few telephone calls had been permitted after much frowning and requesting a short report as to why telephoning was necessary.

During February 1915 the initial training finished. Edwin left the Isle of Wight with his compatriots for two weeks leave, at home. The horses were left at the barracks. He spoke to the stable lads about careful handling of Morvah. Leaving his mount was difficult for all of his life he had lived close to his horses.

Edwin returned to the land for two weeks. His sisters being quite overwhelmed to see the uniformed soldier return. Martha met the train and rode side saddle from the station alongside her pedestrian brother. The girls were fascinated by their brother, proudly displaying his crown with lion royal crest, and his changed demeanour.

Trevelyn Senior very quickly put his son back to work. The routine showed no sign of abating: seven-day milking twice daily together with all of the other work; chapel on Sunday, when newspapers were not allowed. This was a strict routine. Though when it came time to leave home again there would be tears this time.

The news from France and Belgium had not been good. Large numbers of casualties were reported, local families were losing sons. Cornwall being Cornwall, news spread remarkably quickly.

For a few days though Martha's dressage training occupied her brother's thoughts. Her adherence to that most classical form of riding established by the ancient Greeks to both improve the effectiveness of their cavalry, and for artistic and pleasurable purposes. Cavalry General Xenhophon's three books and one by Simon of Athens laid down principles that were being followed here. She had further studied 'L'Ecole de Cavalarie' a source of contemporary practice and knowledge. Combined with her natural flair, this study had taken her to represent Cornwall in national competitions. With the demise of many royal courts throughout Europe it was left to civil stables, and particularly farming people to carry on the discipline. Martha was further enthused by the inclusion of dressage within the Olympic Games of 1912 in Stockholm. Happily the equable climate of south Cornwall and southerly facing slopes of her father's land combined to allow practice outside for most of the year.

Edwin preferred hacking out to the rigidity of dressage. Changing scenery and circumstance suited him. Either way Trevelyn's progeny were skilled in equine matters and could round up and corral cattle from horseback, an asset given the acreage sometimes covered.

Certain fields belonging to Chyancelt Farm were situated on the south side of the River Fal and accessible only by the King Harry ferry. The steers and sheep were taken there. Trevelyn Senior had imported fine Guernsey and Jersey cattle for his own herd and for selling on to other farms. It was important to keep the newly purchased animals several fields away from the main farm initially; for the purpose of quarantine. He subsequently invited potential customers onto his land to observe, inspect and buy. At other times he drove them to Truro market. He preferred however to allow the fine animals to relax, graze and be in their natural habitat during a sale.

In addition to the Channel Island cattle he milked Montgomeryshire, Pembroke and Glamorgan cows, but they were dying out fast. Though commonplace in the 19th century, these were destined to be either extinct or unpopular by the end of the current world war. Trevelyn switched to Devons and Ruby Reds, with mid-length horns, their agility suited the hills and slopes beside the many Cornish rivers.

The soldiers leave was over. Goodbyes said; a few tears were shed. Trevelyn Senior addressed his only son in serious terms: "Fear God, honour the King. Stand straight, keep clean."

Giving his son a small King James bible he implored his rather skeptical offspring to read it, particularly Psalm 35, then Psalm 118. Finally he left his only son with the words of a Cornish favourite, John Wesley: "Do all the good you can, by all the means you can, in all the ways you can, in all the places you can, at all the times you can, to all the people you can, as long as you ever can."

That is how a devout man of the land bade farewell to his family. Clutching his railway warrant Trevelyn saluted his father and began the walk back to Truro Station, accompanied by sister Martha. They talked about the farm, their father's driven attitude towards everything, demanding success, born out of hard work and fear of the Lord God. The soldier suppressed his desire to discuss his father too deeply, not wishing to leave any more concerns about his future than existed already.

"Just tell father for me, not Molly Polwithal," said Edwin kissing his sister on the cheek. "Understand?" Martha just looked at her younger brother and sighed.

Edwin rode the train from Truro back to the Isle of Wight encampment. There displayed upon a board were details of his posting. Disgusted at being sent to Harwich, a major embarkation point for the continent, he asked to speak to an officer with a view to requesting a post at the front.

"No chance," said the major. "Your duties are as specified assisting with embarkation of horses, care of horses and guard duties along the coastal area from horseback. It has been noted how you have a mind of your own young man. You are a free spirit of independent mind and inclined to take decisions arbitrarily. Those decisions are for ranks above you Trevelyn. Your initiative is commendable upon your father's farm; you were schooled for it too. However, until you accept the army way of doing things, with less question, you are a menace to yourself and others too. Understood?"

"Yes sir," replied Edwin.

"Excellent young man. Keep your nose clean and ask again around September," said the major allowing a smile to ease across his face.

"Yes sir, thank you sir," replied Trevelyn, fully reading the older man's train of thought and subtle way of handling the matter.

So it was the Cornish Yeomanry moulded the spirit and ways of another maverick who with his natural zest and fine horsemanship could be of so much use if channelled correctly. The British army certainly knew how to handle such enthusiasm. Immature judgment of youth required moulding into a team effort, then directing.

A routine with some variance now developed. Supervising the arrival of horses, checking their condition, reporting to the veterinary surgeon any problems or vices. With his intuitive knowledge Trevelyn was perhaps more detailed in his analysis. He was after all experienced in dealing with horse traders and farmers when picking out the best horses to buy and which ones to reject. These examinations were more prosaic in nature. A mount exhibiting 'dishing' for example — a fault resulting in the toes turning inwards as it moved forwards — would be rejected for racing or show jumping purposes, but the fault did not prevent army usage.

There is a saying: 'No foot, no horse.' In civil life where the conformation of the animal is of such importance this was applicable, however matters were relegated to the general serviceability of the horse, given the army's current needs. Heavy horses, or shires that were leaving the land could be enlisted straightaway.

Edwin's routine also consisted of guard duties, happily riding his own mount along the shoreline with another, using binoculars to look for any sign of invasion or unusual maritime activity. Harwich and its environs are flatlands, the periphery of the British Services Centre, offering long and wide expanses of view. They had plenty of time to consider any stranger. Not that many appeared. Curious local youths perhaps. 'Fritz' as the Germans were sometimes derisively referred to as, no.

Harwich offered little by the way of entertainment; public houses and fine quality fish and chips aside. The coastal villages of the Naze were of academic interest to a west countryman who was used to an altogether harsher terrain. Colchester, the Roman town, formally home of Bodicia, a well remembered Anglo Saxon Queen a garrison town with its notorious military jail bearing a formidable reputation, offered music hall. Every other Saturday men were given a pass to catch a service bus to the town and sample the exotic delights of burlesque; that bawdy naughtiness provided a particular form of entertainment. Quite an eye-opener to a son of Truro. The Cornwall Philharmonic Society was never like this!

So it was that long hours of work produced colleagues who developed into pals who were good company to socialise with. A drink, with banter, witticisms, merrymaking with their own kind; a culture at ease with itself. A civilisation of people united in purpose against evil, certain of the proven decency of their own country with its customs and practice now spread worldwide by a civilising empire, were determined in their resolution. Socialising and working duties were both easy under such circumstances. Discipline of troops under these conditions was easy too.

The foreigner, with his instinct for control of and distrust in his own population, his unelected cliques who with their claques suppressed, cajoled, indeed controlled volatile characters within their populace when they expressed themselves with insurrection as the only form of resistance to an overwhelming dictatorship and bureaucracy.

British political, economic, judicial, parliamentary and spiritual practices gave respect to the individual. Its sporting culture, 'playing the game', then with teams of cricketers, footballers and rugby players being amiable within a public house or clubhouse, turned its back upon caste and exclusion. Talent with innovation moved forward; governmental progress with a glorious revolution and the first industrial revolution had nurtured great invention. Countries within Old Europe for example were too often busy occupying each other's homeland. The instability created by loss of country with its institutions had retarded Europe, compared to Britain. Why invest in anything when next year it can be taken back from you? No wonder American President Wilson had solemnly warned against taking sides; given old continental Europe's desire for crazy ideology, pogroms and massacres. Their populations quite naturally fled to the new manifestation of Great Britain — America.

CHAPTER III

The battle of Neuve Chappelle had drawn to a close. Intelligence reports were concluding that another battle had been prepared for around the area of Ypres. The previous autumn the whole area of West Flanders had seen battles, including Messies, Armentieres and the Yser, together with Ypres. One identified weak point was that of intelligence. Somehow the Allies needed to coordinate better and obtain more information as telegraphs had broken down; pigeons and rocket devices were all very well but the Germans were also using dogs for the conveyance of a large quantity of information. Maps, plans, written orders, and photographs needed to pass into the right hands and over perhaps twenty miles travelling distance; motorcycles with panniers, indeed all vehicles generally were ideal. Yet the tried and trusted horseman with saddlebags and satchels had for centuries got through. Man and horse together were very effective. Kings and queens of Scotland and England had managed for hundreds of years using this method between Edinburgh and London.

Field commanders in Flanders now put out a request for suitable horsemen; reliable, trustworthy and mature, yet with a spirit that would carry them through the mud, slush and cold of the winter. Those flatlands experienced a wind chill far in excess of normal recorded temperatures. Just as in the British fens carrot crops may be seeded three times before they germinated due to strong winds, in Flanders too the weather determined if progress was to be achieved.

One morning Edwin Trevelyn was ordered to report to the colonel's office. Naturally wondering why such a senior officer required the company of a junior. Had he made a mistake in examining the horses, or whilst on guard duty? Whenever he spotted a veterinary problem he made notes and reported it. His animal husbandry was actually superior to most of those around; surely he had not missed a skin disease and necessity for isolation or special diet, or mud fever, or laminitis in one of the ponies who were particularly susceptible. No surely not because vets were actually asking of him questions regarding practical equine problems. What else could it be then, as all of his guard duties were conducted in sobriety?

The colonel was delayed; his aide-de-camp carried on filing papers as Edwin was told to sit over in a corner. Suddenly the door opened and he jumped to his feet, rigid and nervous, but it was just a major with some papers for 'his nibs'. Then later a ponderous colonel walked slowly into the office taking a straight line through to his own room, looking neither left or right just said, "Follow me Trevelyn, and close the door please young man."

The older man was clearly engrossed. He tweaked and twiddled his moustache, lightly pulled his nose several times then cleared his throat. "Hmmm, hmmm, hmmm," as his throat cleared, his eyes met those of Trevelyn. "We have a problem. Intelligence, lack of actually, not getting through to the right people; no good for planning, logistics, that sort of thing. Need the movement of up-to-date information to be delivered to the front, and back to field headquarters. Can you do it?"

"Sorry Sir, do what?" replied Trevelyn.

"Ride man, ride like a bat out of hell, morning noon and night. Ride from Furnes down the highway across the River Yser to Ypres then back again, keeping the security panniers and satchels dry despite the weather, potential snipers, and sometimes terrible conditions. Frankly Trevelyn you were recommended to me from a number of sources for your temperament, determination, spirit, and not giving up when put to a challenge. We have, due to the security issues involved, taken a careful look at your background. You are clearly made of sound stuff. We visited your father who only wanted to talk about cattle. Cattle I say! With a war on! Will you travel to France with your horse and by yourself, sometimes with others, be a mounted courier? It's the adventure that you asked for, though a very lonesome task on occasions. You understand the importance of this. Sometimes you will have to commit verbal information to memory and then be debriefed at the other end. Other times you must use your instinct for travelling around a strange terrain to circumnavigate the battle, floods, deep mud and so forth. Can you do it lad?"

Lifting a file from the tray he opened it and with his fountain pen hovering over a page he waited for an answer.

"Yes sir, thank you sir." By the time he had finished speaking the colonel had already written 'Second Lieutenant Edwin Trevelyn, Cornish Yeomanry' anticipating the response.

"There could be promotion in this lad, get it right and the British army will show its gratitude. You are to be nominally seconded to the Royal Horse Artillery and my opposite number Colonel Fortescue. We were at school together you know; he was good at rugby football, hopeless at Latin do not tell him I told you so; but he loves his scoff, that is food, and plenty of it; so you will dine well when at barracks in Furnes. Prepare to leave in seventy-two hours. Good luck. Good luck lad," said the colonel, resuming the same gait as upon entry he walked out of his office through the A.D.C.'s office carrying the file; announcing "Scoff" as he passed two officers engrossed over a file.

Trevelyn returned into the late winter leaden atmosphere, the two officers following his passage open mouthed then looking at each other not understanding why they had no knowledge of what was going on. The A.D.C had not been briefed and wanted to know but had no opportunity to find out. Others would ask what was going on but potential gossip had been staunched.

Trevelyn now began his preparations for the journey to France by sea. He had the blacksmith re-shoe the horse. Morvah was 'hot shoed', the shoes being specially made to fit the feet; composed of hardened metal of the type used with studs. Since arriving at Harwich, and despite using his hunter, an Irish Draught thoroughbred cross, for duties, Trevelyn had maintained the horse's fitness including by lunging him on a line. Whilst not riding him, the horse is controlled with a long rein to his head and moves in a circle around the person lunging him. It is essential to lunge both clockwise and counter-clockwise to evenly exercise and build muscle power. Or if repairing particular muscles it may be carried on in just one direction.

Then the soldier paid particular attention to his kit. Boots especially were important; to keep dry feet he worked on the leather over and over again building a mirror shine upon them to withstand the foulest of weather conditions. Horse and man fully prepared, the pair were duly embarked upon a troop ship; along with many other men and horses, mules, carts of varying sizes, lorries, vans, motorcycles with machine guns mounted alongside them, artillery pieces, and provisions for both man and beast.

It was late winter now. March can be rough when crossing the channel. It did not disappoint. Trevelyn had taken ships to the Channel Islands many times, accompanying his father to buy cattle. Further, trips to the Scilly Isles had well prepared him for sea-going exploits. Many were on board a ship for the first time and duly emptied the contents of their stomachs over the leeward side. Some went further, bringing up bile; a particularly unpleasant experience; subsequently drinking only water yet it would react as though put into a hot frying pan and be thrown straight back up again. The low groans from many directions were like chants by Russian Orthodox priests intent upon their devotions. Only the tunes and smells were different. In fact, incense was much needed!

Ideally the crossing would have been to Ostend, however that was impossible. Dunkirk was not the ideal or obvious port but the circumstance of war dictated its use. Once out into the straits of Dover and beyond the coastline of Britain the crossing was assisted by a prevailing wind. Dunkirk was sufficiently behind Allied lines for the Royal Navy shipping to provide escort cover from the German navy. The journey had been made during darkness hours. Upon arrival the animals were taken ashore but the hardware and vehicles were left until daylight.

Disembarking, Trevelyn immediately came under the command of a Major Duncan of the Royal Horse Artillery. The grouping assembled included fresh troops and those returning from leave. Preparing to embark were injured men and those entiteled to annual leave.

Trevelyn initially busied himself with caring for Morvah, who showed no ill effects from the crossing or the ensuing bustle going on around him. Sufficient fresh water, a cake of hay, and a coarse mix of bran, oats, flaked maize with linseed, molasses and cod liver oil contented him. The cod liver oil provided a fine conditioner, good for his coat; molasses provided easily assimilated energy — the arduous work coming would tax his strength and durability. In addition roots and fruit that were putrifying were taken away from the human food stores and added to the equine diet. Apples, turnips, swede and carrots sometimes became available. A salt lick hung on a wall for communal use.

Major Duncan drew together selected mounted troops, of disparate backgrounds, and ordered them to hack the fifteen miles west to Furnes or Veurne. They had the day to get there; expected at 1600 hours. He indicated where certain water troughs were to be found along the route, further advising that the roadside grass was poor due to the time of year and sheer volume of horses and mules that had travelled the route since the previous September.

The men left in high spirits; they found the going straightforward. It was wet — grey leaden skies, expected at that time of year apparently, persisted. Some vehicles passed them, mostly travelling west, but a few moving east. The roadsides were now chewed up and much of the side of the road covered in crushed horse droppings.

Their arrival at Furnes was not greeted with any kind of fanfare. Three of the group, including Trevelyn, were told by the camp guard to report to a certain building. A single-storey brick- built former isolation ward was being used by Colonel Fortescue and his planning team, representing several regiments of British troops, together with representatives from the French army. The French infantrymen in blue coats and scarlet trousers seemed equipped in the style of the Napoleonic era. The British had earlier passed around a quotation with a derogatory implication, quite literally as the French arrived. "Hold hard, the dandies are coming!" In earlier times it had been passed from one British soldier to another down the line to describe the French mousquetaeries under Marshall Saxe, they being celebrated for their foppery. It was a morale boost for the British to snigger about the French.

Fortescue had present certain people from military intelligence with their leather satchels crammed full. The three newcomers were initially ordered to wait in the ante room with two doors between them and the senior officers. Presently they were visited by an aide-de-camp of superior disposition, who stated that the meeting would continue for an unspecified time. Meals had been ordered and they were not to be disturbed. The three horsemen were to properly stable their mounts, find their accommodation and go to the mess. They would be found there or in the lounge if needed, before 2200 hours. Failing that they should report to the A.D.C's office after breakfast at 0800 hours, having fed and prepared their horses for work.

Both horses and men were quartered then fed and watered. The three men retired to the lounge nervously watching every soldier's movement through the room in case he was there to summon them. With so much brass ensconced, they were terrified of annoying them by not being instantly available. The call did not come, so around 2230 hours they left details of their sleeping quarters with several auxiliary staff, checked their horses and retired for the night.

In the morning they rose, washed and shaved then attended their horses before finding breakfast. As they ate the aide-de-camp of a superior disposition walked by; without even glancing at them he ordered them to report to Colonel Fortescue's suite in ten minutes and then walked on. He left the impression that the three were of little consequence. His own appearance gave the impression more of a mannequin than a working soldier. "It must surely be tough at field headquarters," quipped one. All agreed, grinning.

The colonel's secretary held the men until his aide-de-camp used the intercom phone to call for them to enter his own area. It was empty when they entered. Subsequently the aide appeared from the Colonel's suite and without looking up, more in the form of an announcement said, "Colonel Fortescue will see you now, but he is very busy," he stated, in a very off hand manner. The three entered, where the atmosphere was different. The Colonel ordered his aide to bring four of the French-style coffees that he liked and to close the door. The aide with eyes wide, unblinking, replied, "Yes sir," and delivered the same order to the secretary when he returned to his own area. Shaking each horseman by the hand — unusual for a military greeting — the Colonel thanked the three men for agreeing to the seconded posting.

"Now to business gentlemen," he said. "Everything that I say to you will, mark my words, will be treated in the strictest confidence. You discuss the following with no one understand, no one else."

"Yes sir," chimed the men.

"I will eventually pass you on to Major Browne who represents military intelligence. He was present at yesterday's meeting with the French, and will for the time being be your point of contact. That is not to say that I will not be present at any briefings or indeed de- briefings involving yourselves. You have all been picked out as gutsy types; your horsemanship is enviable; your fitness combined with willingness commendable. Further you are ahem, how shall I say, bloody minded mavericks. I need determination, initiative, the instincts of a lone operator yet part of a team. You understand?"

"Yes sir," chimed the threesome.

"Frankly gentlemen we have a problem, yes upon my word a potentially serious problem."

A knock was heard on the door. "Come!" boomed the Colonel. The aide-de-camp stiffly placed the four large coffee bowls down, along with milk, sugar and biscuits.

"Presents from Mrs Miranda Fortescue, my wife," said the Colonel with a sad distant tone.

"Will that be all sir?" said the aide.

"Thank you Carr, I will call you if I need anything. See that we are not disturbed, other than Major Browne, who is to be sent in."

"Yes sir," responded the aide, shutting the door

They shared out the coffees. "Goats milk today," said the Colonel sniffing the milk. "Never mind it is good for psoriasis! Drink up," he added. There was an obsession where food and drink were concerned; it pleasured him. Perhaps he was thinking of his wife's or mother's cooking. Gratitude for good food, compared to that consumed at boarding school! The army gave no reason for complaint about food. It boosted morale, and could be substantial as well as nourishing

"Now to business; come to the table," said the Colonel beckoning the three over. "The potentially serious situation is this. We had a series of four battles around Flanders last October and November, and one at

Neuve Chapelle earlier this month as you well know. What you do not know is that our communications broke down; our intelligence left much to be desired and we suffer from a lack of ammunition. One of these might be very serious; the combination of all three is potentially disastrous. We have photographs being taken of the enemy sites. Reconnaissance is being carried on from land, air and sea, but we fear gas attacks now. Our superior musketry with fifteen aimed shots per minute is comforting, but not against gas. The Ypres Salient area encompassing such villages and small towns as Pilckem, Poelcapaelle, Passchandale, Brookseinde, and Artmentieres is building up for another bad one. It's the only piece of Belgium we have left; if we get pushed back the Hun will control Flanders, Arras Amiens and the River Somme crossings. The French will lose their nerve; with Paris then only two days march away, I dread to think what will happen".

"The French are frankly, very, very worried. So to counteract bad weather, vehicle breakdown and impassability and low ammunition levels, expect the unexpected I say. Assuming telegraphs fail, carrier pigeons and the odd dog too, I propose to back myself up with a tried-and-tested method of communication that formed the backbone of diplomacy and intelligence exchange for centuries. A man on a horse.

"You men will take our satchels and saddle bags containing maps, plans, written instructions, photographs and coded orders, down the road to advance field headquarters at Ypres, then to and from the field commanders in the trenches. Put quite simply you will provide me with an unbroken link between senior commanders, on the assumption that all other communication has ceased. You will ride back here to Furnes, ideally along the service road, but when necessary back across the open countryside, reporting to myself and Major Browne. Your knowledge of the Ypres Salient and West Flanders must become both intuitive and spontaneous for the purposes of your own survival".

"You see, the war is changing the way men battle for territory and ideology. The Germans are pursuing an official policy of Schrecklichkeit, that is 'frightfulness', in order to cow down the Belgian people. The French are terrified of a breakthrough of the current line or deep entry into their territory."

"We have well documented instances of wholesale destruction of property and stock together with the killing of civilians, even Crucifixion, throughout Belgium. The Belgian army is in a state of transition, from essentially a volunteer force to a fully conscript army. Whilst delaying the Hun at canal bridges and railway tunnels they are no match for the efficient war machine and 'frightfulness' emanating from Berlin. Remember your history men, civilians traditionally play a spectator role in these matters; they cannot deter air raids from military airships. Furthermore the aeroplane is being quickly developed for air raiding."

"We are, I stress, very concerned about the unprovoked break of all chivalrous rules, especially if Germany launches gas canisters at us. We can neither protect ourselves , the civil population or their animals. Those who are not killed may be starved out. Dreadful, dreadful I say. This was going to be over by Christmas past. Huh! A swift return to peace is even further away now."

"The politicians in London are creating a new ministry. The Ministry of Munitions, the press have got hold of stories about lack of ammunition at the front line. Mr Asquith appears in some political difficulties. He clearly knows that there will be much more killing before we are done, mark my words."

"Now, you men are to assist with a range of equine requirements around this encampment during the next few days. Prepare yourself, your horse and kit for riding around the future battle zones. Major Browne is due back soon from Ypres, having met with General Ferdinand Foch's representative. The gathering intelligence is suggesting that during this month of April we may again meet the Hun here in West Flanders. Use this down-time productively men. Eat and sleep well. Be at hand, ready for earnest briefing and consequential action. You are for now dismissed."

He gave a nervous broad smile, a longing look. A collective "Thank you sir," followed. The three then left.

They now entered a few days of a sort of pseudo war. Urgent preparations were occurring all around them. Canadian regiments were arriving; some former Royal Canadian Mounted Police provided good company. Together with certain British mounted troops they conducted horse races, with bets on the side for first, second and third places! Additionally, bets could be placed on potential falling jockeys! The ground was soft, ploughed soil. Nearly as soft as the fens of Lincolnshire and Cambridgeshire. Falling upon the land was not the problem, with the going heavy and pace slow. However the races alleviated the boredom. Winnings were then almost inevitably bet on cards after dinner. It provided some amusement. Participants were however warned not to make lame or damage in any way their horses; the penalty would be cookhouse chores, cleaning of the latrines or a similar unpopular duty.

A good working and social rapport was built between all, which was essential given the way in which these men were intended to interact. They joked about everything, including 'bully beef' in tins, and the biscuits. The sometimes indifferent water; a rush to the swamp when showers or baths were possible. The necessity for several men to bath communally in a barrel. Sleeping in clothes when on exercise, and lack of sleep when ammunition had to stay belted on. Lectures on everything from lice and venereal disease to military requirements for varying circumstances. The travelling concerts passing through. The YMCA — Young Men's Christian Association — with refreshments and a game of billiards.

There were around 80,000 men in the vicinity now, plus the hospitals. A cavalry parade ground had emerged, as had small gardens planted with flowers and vegetables. The agrarian urges of some created a pastoral scene. They planted gardens replicating some of the beautiful efforts of the railway company staff, along station platforms back home. Improving the environment was so natural, so instinctive.

Sometime around the 12th of April, Trevelyn together with his two mounted colleagues who met upon arrival in France, Andrews from Flint and Murray from Rutland, were called in to see Major Browne. He briefed them on a small job requiring dispatch riders delivering and collecting intelligence. Little did the three men know at this time that it was essentially just a test to see how those operations worked in practice. The three of them were to ride together, leaving the encampment at Furnes crossing the River Yser. Then at Oostvleteren Andrews would break off for Poperinge, make his delivery to a small outpost then back to Rosebrugge-Haringe, over the Belgian/French border, then turning right to follow country roads up to Ghyvelde and back to Furnes. Murray was to hack to Ypres and the forward garrison there near to a communication trench, deliver his package, and use the main road home. Trevelyn would break off at Oostvleteren, picking up byways travel to Langemark after which en-route to Zonnebeke he would find an outpost to where his package must be delivered. His journey would take him on to Ypres, meeting with Murray and returning back along the main road to Furnes together. All three were expected to collect items for Colonel Fortescue from those with whom they liaised. They would further wait at their various destinations for as long as the relevant officer required them to. Throughout, they were expected to take careful note of future 'hidie holes'. Barns, buildings, houses, ditches, spinneys, woods, anywhere that may afford a respite should they find themselves unexpectedly within enemy territory. During a battle, the enemy might break the line and surge forward, thus stranding a lone horseman behind the new lines. In that instance it may be necessary to hole up, bury the satchels and saddlebags, only carrying such verbal intelligence as had been imparted, then await their chance to make an escape, or at worst anticipate capture by the Germans

Their instinct for survival and sixth sense were being tested. Animal cunning was being honed. The road from Furnes to Ypres was overladen with traffic. Lorries of men and supplies; heavy horses transporting cookers; motorcycles and bicycles; marching men with heavy backpacks, artillery pieces, indeed all of the paraphernalia of war for an army on the move. Sometimes a diesel lorry or Red Cross wagon would pass them; the horse drawn vehicles were slower.

Andrews completed his mission first and returned very late at night. He caused some confusion to the garrison duty guards. Because his mission was not generally known about they were reluctant to admit him. Major Browne had to be summoned to verify his tale

Murray had the easiest test and waited overnight at Ypres for his colleague. Trevelyn was hacking along the front line and encountered a number of communication trenches which led to second line support trenches, thence on to the front line and fire bays. He was able to speak with many duty guards: everyone wanted to talk. A hearty welcome was given as they all hoped the rider was couriering news to withdraw! Such opportunity to gossip was always worth a square of chocolate, a shared biscuit, or perhaps a toffee. Goodies that had been sent from home in parcels were exchanged for not just other goodies but for information too. As with politics, information was the easiest traded currency. Trevelyn had little for them though, especially due to the rigidity of his orders, silence being the order of this and every ensuing mission. Meeting up with Murray at Ypres they were both fed and watered, doing the same for their horses. Accommodated in camouflage tents they slept happily on straw mattresses.

Following breakfast they waited for their contact officer to release them. During the morning they were loaded with paperwork then called in separately for briefing; details of verbal communications that were to be conveyed to either Major Browne or Colonel Fortescue. It was only then that they realised how this expedition had been as much an exercise as practical training. Each man was given unique information and told not to repeat it to the other. The information was all relevant to the war effort; but this was a test also.

Having been briefed the men were ordered to speed their way back to Furnes. Upon their arrival at Furnes garrison the horsemen were told by the guard to report to Major Browne, who saw them immediately. As they approached his office area they came upon Andrews who was now summoned to also attend.

The men were called in one at a time to explain everything that had been committed to memory. It quickly became evident to Major Browne and his juniors that there had been no attempt at communication between the men. They were roundly congratulated on their discretion. Further discussion took place regarding their observations on the countryside. Looking out for German scouts behind Allied lines was part of their remit. The three men were subsequently encouraged to spend time in one another's company exchanging knowledge regarding the physical characteristics of the Ypres Salient; indeed anything of West Flanders that came to their knowledge. For an unknown length of time they were destined to ride its highways, byways and cart tracks. They needed local knowledge.

Above all, Trevelyn was a stock man. His intimate knowledge and love of the animal gave him a dimension which made him sought after and interesting to listen to. Similarly his fluency regarding the many bovine breeds was impressive and valuable, but not in this context! During a few spare hours at the garrison he took time to study any and all horse flesh represented there. His own horse Morvah was an Irish Draught and thoroughbred cross. He was fast, very fit with physical and mental stamina, courageous, with sound legs, strong shanks, heels and large cannon bone. The larger legs came from his Irish Draught breeding. He had a kind and generous eye with a knowing look. His vices were simply not developed, even if they existed. Viewing other men's mounts Trevelyn took careful notes pertaining to breeds represented in the stables and grazing around the periphery.

The Hackney horse is a high-stepping Harness horse. It has great courage and ability. It descended from the French Trotter, a beautiful racehorse descended themselves from a selective breeding with Norfolk Roadsters. The cold-blooded Friesian, descended from the primitive European forest horses. The Romans had used them; Knights riding to the crusades too. Here they were being used for a difficult crusade albeit no less savage. Irish Draught horses were well represented in their own right. Known as 'the horse of the countryside' their versatility made them very useful.

There were Cleveland Bays, Dutch Gelderlanders, Dutch Warmbloods, the smaller French Warmbloods, the hardy and stocky Arigeois from the Pyrennes. Welsh mountain ponies were there too. A number of heavy horse breeds were busy at work. The Flanders mud and slurry were a problem but roads and hard tracks allowed pulling of kitchen equipment, artillery trucks and all manner of supplies by Shire horses, those seventeen-hand giants that paired together can pull fifty tons.

Trevelyn was familiar with these magnificent beasts from the farm. Despite certain mechanisation four Shires were needed too. He noticed Suffolk Punch horses, a routine farm horse and the rather pretty Belgium/ French Ardennais, a smaller cart horse. The Belgian Draught horse or Brabant known as the Flanders horse were visible, and ideal for work in this part of the world. The Germans and Central European powers used many other breeds indigenous to their parts of the world. It was truly a source of fascination to the farmer and horseman to learn about so many breeds and ride a few of them. A welcome relief during a generally difficult time.

April progressed and so did the riding trips around the Allied-held parts of West Flanders. Intelligence to and from the trenches gleaned from around the area provided by what minimal civilian population remained was all ferried to and fro. Although a certain duplication occurred using the telegraph and vehicular convoys together with miniature rockets and pigeons, Colonel Fortescue was delighted with his 'belt and braces' option, believing that a man on horseback would ultimately beat both the weather, terrain and enemy, or whatever tried to overcome him. It was just a question of picking the right men for the job; those who had the all round aptitude.

As the pressure built during early April, a sense that an impending conflict was not long away developed. Information was circulated on a 'need to know' basis; after that the rumour mill ground its course. The food was quite good at Furnes, morale therefore high. Unquestionably the two were linked. Around this time Trevelyn began thinking of his home, father and greater family. Family events concentrated his mind. Their letters were encouraging. Agnes was now engaged to a farmer from the Penzance area and to be married during June. Martha was, to quote father's cowman Zebadiah, "A courting strong," which implied an exclusion of all other potential suitors. In actual fact she was preparing for her own wedding. Charlotte was still trying to organise everyone as usual. Everything seemed to benefit from her bossing, so she thought.

The soldier thought about his plans after the war, for his own farm with a prize herd of cattle. Animals were his love. Would father insist upon him staying on Chyancelt Farm? Could he afford his own property? Would a farm become available nearby along the banks of the River Fal, or east around Tresillion? So many uncertainties gripped him. His Celtic spirit of independence certainly gripped him. Inspired by the bards, Cornwall was to him and his family an idea which lit the world. The Isle of Avalon perhaps. Or was it Avillon? King Arthur's burial place. The tale of myth is so powerful that we will it to be true. Myths of identity, myths of state, myths handed down by the bards that were sung about and spoken of in the alehouses and market places. How many layers did a myth have? Did not the ancient Greeks of Great Helens with their myths exert the same pressure upon their own within their islands and without, around their diaspora — dispersed colonies of Greeks — within the many city states. The Illiad, the Odyssey, Aneas and Dido. Was not Carthage real? Surely so.

Romulus and Remus, those legendary founders of Rome suckled by a she-wolf, had created brilliance out of potentially nothing. Virgil, born in a ditch due to his mother's unexpected labour had succeeded greatly, despite remaining something of a wanderer. Trevelyn had wandered voluntarily into this war, yet was hearing the call of the land, from his own known ancestor's tillage of soil around crack and coombe in Cornubia, 'Land of the Saints'. That land of King Arthur and his round table. Of St Petroc 'Chief of all the Saints'. He thought about the miracle and morality plays written in the vernacular, Cornwall's native language, defunct since 1799. The mystique that emanates from the writing within 'Beunans Meriasek', and the 'Odinalia' charting 'The Origin of the World, the Passion of our Lord and his Resurrection'.

The pull upon his being and psyche was touching his core. Cornwall was calling; it seemed to use every device available to pull his thoughts back to home. It permeated the letters from the girls, and his father. Wrapped around the posted gifts of brawn and hazelet meats from the farm made by Agnes or Mary-Lee and the sheepskin coat from his father were invocations from that sainted land Cornwall, anticipating his return. Also there was secular news too, and gossip from the chapel. Truro school, the livestock market, dead stock sales, the neighbours, local birth and death all provoked anecdotes; committed to paper by pen.

Always within the family communications were biblical references. Acts 2-17: "I will give my spirit to everyone. Your young men will see visions and your old men have dreams." It was a just war they all believed in; the decency of British institutions must be upheld and strengthened. "Long live the King."

A very kind parcel arrived for Trevelyn from the Queen Alexandra Field Force Fund. Unexpected, he received with gratitude the towel, mittens, shoe laces, sleeping helmet, soap, handkerchief and toilet paper from their charity. A practical gift from appreciative people.

The Germans, it was rumoured, were moving their troops to the eastern front. Naturally morale surged as the word spread of abandonment of the western trenches. A few days of relaxed antipathy was broken on the 22nd of April with heavy shelling from the German side.

Following conventional shelling Fortescue had called for Trevelyn and his two colleagues, to brief them on his current requirements. Each were given orders separately, the content of which was unknown to the others. They were on their own this time.

Trevelyn was to immediately tack up, prepare for several days of riding with uncertain arrival at any destination but required to report to the senior duty officer at a number of forward trenches around the Ypres Salient; delivering orders with intelligence; collecting any casualty news and frontline knowledge of the enemy and its future intentions. Further, he was to check around a number of villages that he would pass through and ask about spies or German scouts. Had any person been through asking questions regarding the war, or creating a conversation with regard to the Allies and their activities? The village shops, post offices and tap rooms being of special interest for these enquiries

Leaving Furnes within 90 minutes of his receiving his orders, in pouring rain and cold, Trevelyn journeyed north east of the Ypres Road. It seemed desolate; grey skies, drizzle, rain then more drizzle. He checked into the guard position at the head of two trenches, being required to untack Morvah each time, giving the horse the opportunity to stretch, drink and relax. The soldier collected his first army B104.83 forms — 'Posted as Missing' — which resonated with the young man

There were several trench emplacements of a French Territorial division, who were to be waved at, but unless an emergency occurred, passed by.

As he approached the first one Trevelyn noticed that soldiers were running away from the line in a southerly and southwest direction as though pursued by something or someone. They were tearing at their necks, coughing, spluttering, choking, gasping for breath. They had evidently abandoned their guns, and their posts. A panic had overtaken those men. The British yeoman soldier would later understand that the Germans had released chlorine gas from cylinders. Those inhaling it directly died extremely painful deaths. The men who survived fled in panic; they had no protection.

The Germans had cut a swathe in the Allied lines. A blue and white mist drifted with the prevailing wind as the gap opened; then gradually the intensity of shelling increased. The Allies needed to prevent a German push through the gap. Trevelyn moved quickly to get out of the area where men were coughing; he rode on using the soft grassy verges to enable greater speed. He and Morvah were constrained by the heavy going. Verges had been churned up by large vehicles. Where property had been demolished by earlier shelling a mound of rubble, earth and man-made debris littered the side — sometimes nine or ten feet high. At a crossroads he met a single track railway that was in continual use with very long slow moving trains. He crossed it, acknowledging the signalman in his first storey window.

A soldier was posted to the site as a guard. The hapless Tommy was simply terrified of the post, as it was a clear landmark upon the flatlands for German range finders to set their sights upon. Contenting himself by drawing hard upon a Woodbine cigarette he asked Trevelyn if he carried any chocolate, sweets or anything else to eat. He mentioned seeing other crossing points and railway junctions where giant Hessian or tarpaulin barriers had been erected for a considerable stretch in order to disguise movement. Using tree stumps that stood as a stark beacon, the remnants of once proud mature trees and other wood debris from wrecked houses, a sort of fence supported the protective barrier. It disguised the movement of men and machines sometimes long enough for a convoy to pass. Perhaps it might survive for a few days. The soldier expressed his view that he was a sitting duck and requested that a message be passed on to that effect. Trevelyn agreed.

The soldier was warned by Trevelyn not to talk to strangers. Especially anyone being particularly friendly. German spies were undoubtedly working this patch; a railway crossing was very useful for disrupting the Allied war effort. Trevelyn rode on collecting and delivering his satchels as directed. As evening approached he was taken into a trench. Morvah was stabled by the entrance to the communication trench under a tarpaulin.

Trevelyn walked through the communication trench for a couple of hundred yards on duck boarding — those wooden slats laid to the ground to keep soldiers' feet as dry as possible under the circumstances. A passing point was on one side near to a shell trench junction on the other. Arriving at an officer's shelter he was given necessary sustenance and offered a bunk hole in the wall of the trench, as the officer who used it was on duty until 0700 the next morning. A further exploration of the trench was needed to find the latrines, which were off the communication trench towards the front line and fire bays.

Before retiring he was briefed by a senior officer with information for military intelligence, but to forget it if captured. Together with copious quantities of paperwork for the satchels and saddlebags he now had possession of a considerable amount of sensitive property. It was evident that another slogging match typical of trench warfare was just beginning. Casualties were going to be a major problem. Returning them to Furnes, then perhaps to Dunkirk for transporting to Britain, was a monumental undertaking during battle.

After breakfast the following morning Trevelyn spoke at length with men who fought in the area during the previous October and November, gaining an impression that exactly the same experience was now starting again. How many near identical skirmishes would take place before the war was finished? However, as far as he could see the gas cloud experienced by the French the previous day was a new phenomenon. Trevelyn carefully attended to his mount, checking the feet and with a hoof pick removing all dirt within and around the shoe. He used some of his toilet roll to clean out the horses nostrils and around the eyes. Full grooming was not possible. In the wet conditions the oil secreted from the coronary band in Morvah's hooves was gone. Unfortunately Trevelyn had nothing with which to replace it. Perhaps back in Furnes he could properly treat his horse, to repair the damage caused by the damp. He tacked up and sped on his way back to Furnes, thinking about the condition of his beautiful horse, whilst hearing the sound of guns. As he crossed the River Yser he noticed many craters around the area. Clear attempts had been made by the Germans to cut the link back to Furnes. They had failed, just. Back at the encampment the atmosphere replicated that of a disturbed beehive. Everyone was busy, too preoccupied even to acknowledge the returning yeoman soldier.

Trevelyn reported to Major Browne with his paperwork. He was told to go and attend his horse and prepare to leave again in around three hours. The Major told him to report to the Colonel's office two hours later, ready for instructions. The time available was spent grooming the horse, then himself; he managed a dip in a tub, bathe and shave, then food, before attending Colonel Fortescue's office where Major Browne and three junior officers were present.

The briefing was simple, clear and very disconcerting. Allied casualties were high. The Germans now had the opportunity to push through Allied lines due to chlorine gassing the French. The rain had ensured that movement of men and machines was difficult. Mud clogged everything mechanical and damaged horses' legs and hooves, softening them, which caused breakages, resulting in footsore and lame animals. The Scottish regiments had the folds of their kilts encrusted with mud thus greatly increasing the weight they carried. Boots became heavy, cold with damp, unable to accept polish or dubbin because of saturation. In fact all facets of living conditions were miserable. Morale was low.

It was quite evident that the Germans would continue with this particular battle, centring on Ypres, despite intelligence suggesting that they were moving troops to the eastern front in readiness for a push against the Russians. There appeared to be mounting political instability in Russia centring on St Petersburg and Moscow; radical elements of one group or another were competing for the ear of the population. Withdrawal from the 'Tsar's war' was the rallying cry. Into that febrile atmosphere the Germans appeared to be hastily massing many divisions from the west. Yet here they were giving every indication of being much stronger just when a weakness was sensed. All very worrying. Further, the new gas weapon had clearly affected the psyche of not only the ground level troops but the planners and decision-makers too.

Trevelyn attended his briefing — a rather downbeat session that was fearful of the next few days. His bags were loaded with maps, plans and photographs. The latter had tracing paper overlaid, which showed an interpretation of what was thought to be on the ground. Some piles of very large shells were thought to be gas canisters. It was clear to Trevelyn that he would need the zeal of a missionary to ride around a number of posts in the shortest time possible. During the briefing a messenger came in with a note. Fortescue shared it with Browne; they frowned, exchanged a few words. Fortescue shook the piece of paper at all assembled indicating that the news was unpalatable. Trevelyn was dismissed, urging all speed. He was expected to be away for two nights. Due to the German attack his journeys were unlikely to be along the main roads; he would have to be circumspect with his route, always thinking of his own security.

The horseman remembered to pack his mittens, the toilet roll was so very welcome too. As the winter had lost its grip he decided that the sheepskin coat was not necessary. Leaving the encampment alone he noticed a few remaining townspeople, going about their business as though in a daze, with their heads down, almost oblivious now of the overwhelming

military presence around them, engulfing their lives. Trevelyn would have
preferred to re-shoe Morvah but the speed of his departure and pressure
upon the blacksmith prevented this. He left in drizzle, which as soon as he
urged the horse to a trot caused a stinging sensation to his eyes. Heading
along the main road out of Furnes he turned north across the low lying
fields and land reclaimed from the sea, known as 'polders', to find the
canal route which crossed under the Dixmude Road. His first drop and
collection were just outside the village. By the time he reached the post he
was quite wet. His eyes stung with droplets of rain and the mittens were
soaked through. Cold fingers needed to hold the reins lightly, a difficult act.
Retaining a relaxed posture and perfect balance was vital.

Dixmude had been destroyed by the Germans the previous November.
There were trenches in this area known as Boyau de al Mort, 'trench of
death'; their proximity to German lines giving the Belgians a reason to
invent such a fatalistic name. Due to periodic collapse, because of rain
water pulling them down, a quotation written by someone later to be found
by another, sums up the plight of all those affected.

*"There is water everywhere, in the air, on the ground, under the ground…
It rains for three days out of four in this part of the world and when the rain stops,
the mist rises from the soil, a white mist, almost solid, in which both men and things
look like spectres."*

In this environment a lone horseman was charged with doing his
duty. News that air raids had occurred over Paris as well as Britain, were in
his mind. Zeppelins, those cigar-shaped airships, caused particular fear in
the public mind.

From Lo, Trevelyn followed the canal until it met the River Yser
— the bridge was still intact. A slippery nervous walk across the planks
provided him with a route to Oostvleteren and his second drop and
collection. There, he met groups of men sitting on boxes under tarpaulin
making small bombs; packing explosives into empty food tins and bottles.
The conversation was very amusing, interspersed with serious worried
anecdotes. Their humour drew upon the operetta of Messrs Gilbert
and Sullivan, which was written at the time when Britain was the most
powerful country in the world.

Never had mankind seen such a dominant empire yet here were characters in the great British tradition sticking two fingers up at authority as everything was satirised within a disrespectful chorus. "I am the very model of a modern major-general" was being sung by way of a reflected tease of their own commanding officers. No country had ever previously allowed such irreverence with self deprecation, especially considering the sheer power of the nation. It reflected the moral certainties, security of the governing and bureaucratic classes, and essentially relaxed nature of society.

How fared Nineveh, Rome, Carthage, Alexander, Khan or Napoleon?

The paranoia that affected so many civilisations and especially European countries was absent in Britain with its seafaring island peoples who were naturally outward looking. The Germans were now within two and half miles of Ypres, tragically the townspeople had abandoned their homes. Nervously talking about the chlorine gas, they complained that the Allies were being treated as though vermin; no more than rats. The Germans, they said, were in breach of The Hague Convention of 1899; but who could referee the situation? As attacks commenced, and in the form of a warning, the bells of the Cathedral of Gand rang out loud warning the populace and soldiery. Not the mathematical permutations devised by the likes of Jasper Snowden and Fabian Steadman, but continental European simultaneous clanging. It produced the desired effect. Yet incredibly it was only months since the British and Germans played football together around Christmas time in 1914. That Christmas was to mark the end of the war they said in August. Where was the sense in what was happening? One officer conscript quoted Cyrus: "No man has any business with government who is not himself better than those whom he governs." It was a way of complaining about his predicament and hopelessness for seeing a future. Another complained that they were being measured as though dry goods.

Trevelyn needed to move on. He dried himself and warmed his hands, nevertheless the damp within his clothing would take some considerable time to remove. His boots too were becoming less resistant to water despite excessive spit and polish. As he rode off the Ypres Road towards Langemark he could hear a terrible bombardment to the north east. It resonated from the ground through Morvah into his rider; the horse shook and was clearly wary; being an animal of flight, its instinct would be to run away, jump anything along the route to somewhere else. Even the horse was unable to define exactly what it would be running from. Riding generally in a line parallel with the canal, the only high ground available was the banks of waterways and artificial hillocks created by shelling, which were surrounded by puddles. Where perhaps a line of trees had defined a polder or the path of a canal there were gaunt stumps, looking more like telegraph or electricity poles. A shattered windmill gave memory to economic activity, last used during the previous August, September and October; no harvest involving grain or root would be gathered from this soil for many a season. There was no vegetation, birds or animal life. A grey black soil, muddy puddles, grey sky and generally leaden appearance reflected a similar atmosphere created by the humans present in the area.

The horseman now rode south east following the canal. It was the German side; should the enemy advance he was trapped — hopefully his kith and kin would hold the line, until at least he had an escape route! Ypres town was officially out-of-bounds for encampment, being unsafe, with buildings crumbling everywhere. St Martin's Church, a 13th century icon. The magnificent Cloth Hall from the same era: a market building where men had bargained their agreements or otherwise parted company looking perhaps for a deal elsewhere. Medieval man had made his living, and peace with his creator, within yards of each other. Neither appeared remotely possible now. His next rendezvous was just outside Ypres where he wanted to garrison for the night. He was very anxious to remove his clothing, dry it overnight before journeying to Hooge and Poperinge up to Rosebrugge-Heringe, re-cross the Yser River and return to Furnes. The sight of Ypres had been overwhelming.

Leaving it via the Menin Road, through what had been the Menin Gate, the surreal experience of mounds of rubble either side of the road: stakes protruding that were formerly trees; bricks, stones, beams and shards of metal, scattered over and through the mound creating an abstract impression. The road was covered in dust and rubbish created by violent demolition, showing human and horse footprints together with vehicle tracks. Due to the sheer quantity of men and vehicles, (almost every British Army regiment seemed to be using this particular road at some time), the actual travelling area under dry conditions would have resembled the surface of the moon; under wet circumstances, a slurry of sand, cement and dust — particles of everything that goes to build a town and its infrastructure littered everywhere. Then amongst the travelling multitudes of foot soldiers, wagons, artillery pieces, horses carrying men, towing mobile kitchens, or carts and Red Cross wagons, appeared a sight that was other than worldly. A troupe of a travelling entertainers bringing light music and laughter in their wake. Who would want to laugh under these conditions? How did you make merry in these circumstances? Yet for everything there seemed to be a time...

Outside Ypres, Trevelyn was stopped by an officer, asked about his business and waved on whilst abruptly being told to get off the road if at all possible. He was in the vicinity of 'Hell Fire Corner' an intersection of Menin Road, Ypres to Rouleis Railway, and Potijze to Zillebeke road. His direction was wrong; straying into the town was wrong.

"Curiosity killed the cat, remember," barked the man and pointed to a route in the direction of Hooge, where he would find his overnight stay and dropping or meeting point. Within the hour he had found his contact points; both horse and rider were very pleased to rest up. Having removed the tack from Morvah, Trevelyn immediately lifted the horse's feet and picked out the accumulated rubbish within each hoof. The shoes were showing signs of wear, uneven now; ideally new shoes should be located, but first a blacksmith. The encampment, behind the trench line, offered a straw bed for both horse and rider. He fed Morvah, settled him, then was allowed to feed himself before being debriefed. The communication between those who were questioning and receiving the intelligence and their visitor was curt, yet businesslike. The men based near Ypres were quite clearly on edge. A battle had commenced; they knew not what to expect next, fearful of being cut off without ongoing intelligence and with no answer to gas warfare.

Around dawn, Trevelyn was awoken by a dreadful noise. He jumped to his feet barely awake; a horrible experience, as one needs to have a few moments to pass from sleep through drowsiness into an alert state. Buttoning his tunic he left the tarpaulin and galvanized tin encampment he saw Morvah, as though about to take off; ears pricked, wide-eyed, head jerking from side to side, picking up on the panic that was now engulfing everywhere. The Germans had started a bombardment; the ground shook with a continuous thud, thud, thud, as artillery landed, decibels increased, men shouted. Further towards the trench line shells were landing; clearly a substantial bombardment was underway. It was now imperative that Trevelyn left in order to deliver his last package. The trenches around Hooge needed up-to-date intelligence. Unfortunately there was to be no opportunity to renew his horse's shoes; further, breakfast had proved uninspiring, for all concerned; taken on the hoof, so to speak. He left, pushing biscuits into his mouth, anything to produce a 'full belly' feeling. His journey down to Hooge was quite simply terrifying. Despite pushing and pushing for action whilst based in Harwich as part of the Cornish Yeomanry, he wondered if the two other horsemen, Andrews and Murray, were in the same predicament. En route he passed roadside settlements that were now strange and hideous contortions of their former selves. At one point horses with carts still harnessed to them, their loads piled up, untouched, lay dead in the road. Men lay around either dead or dying, their belongings scattered. The travelling group had been decimated by shelling, over the top of the trenches, aimed particularly at road and rail junctions. Wherever possible hessian and tarpaulin screens were erected to obscure movement, but in this instance they were not available or destroyed. One particular danger for Morvah in a situation such as this was the sheer quantity of wood splinters everywhere. A horse's foot has a v-shaped 'frog' within the hoof; it is nature's device to prevent slipping and absorb shock, being the initial contact the animal has with the ground; a metal or wooden shard pushing up beyond the hoof, quickly festering would render the horse lame. The rider needs to be very alert mentally, in addition to his own physical agility, assisting his mount and avoiding the pitfalls along the route. Riding under such conditions is exhausting. Trevelyn spoke gently to his horse encouraging him on, a kind voice, and clear instructions: those inculcated leg and foot guides telling the horse what is required of him, asking for a response. The essential communication between horse and rider.

During one particular experience of shelling the noise and accumulated tension became simply too much for the horse. Suddenly he rose up on his hind legs, shying; the recoil indicated his reticence to proceed, clearly wanting to dislodge his rider and all baggage, then bolt. Trevelyn sat back and relaxed, let his shoulders drop, his heels drop, raising his toes then just waited at a precarious angle. Slowly, very slowly he felt the horse's muscles relax, then inch by inch Morvah let himself down to the ground. Had the rider panicked, fallen off or jumped off without doubt his mount would have fled. Such were the unfavourable conditions for any and all equine activity.

It was clear that Hooge was close by; the actions of the men and machines was intensifying. Then he saw an event that took a few seconds to comprehend. A line of men walking very close with one hand on the shoulder of the man in front. Some had their heads bowed, some with their chins facing the sky, other heads bobbing; glum uncomprehending expressions on their faces. Some carried rifles in their empty hand, others clung onto the rucksacks of the man in front; many wore blindfolds; all had water bottles, canvas bags and headgear of some type. Their faces were generally yellow, the buttons upon their tunics now green. Soon it was evident that more snakes of men were emerging. Each line was preceded by a fit man, leading them away from the trenches towards Ypres. Eventually, when a truck or horse drawn vehicle arrived they would board it for a long dark journey to Furnes, and back to Britain.

A very disconcerting sight, a new sight in the history of warfare. Gassed men with a very uncertain future. They had been treated at their regimental aid post within the trench; now rounded up they would visit a casualty station. Some were destined for basic surgery, others would have to wait, for a hospital. Arriving at the outer post near to Hooge trenches, the yeoman soldier asked to be taken to his named contact in this instance; there was a certain delay -- because of the man's recent death. A dog emerged from somewhere, known ironically as 'Lucky'. Perhaps every dog staying alive in this company was lucky! She was spoken to and fussed over by nearly everyone. A wooden post nearby was being rubbed up and down by a soldier with lice; like a bear in the wild, his knees bent as he moved himself around, gaining momentarily relief from this pestilence.

Trevelyn entered a few camouflage tents looking for conversation. An easy joke was exchanged; the natural rapport of 'we are all in it together lads' bred a fatalistic black humour. Those who smoked would exchange cigarettes or a bowl of tobacco. Someone might have a few sweets to share from a parcel recently arrived from home. Presently a corporal approached Trevelyn and asked him to proceed up the communication trench to the officer's shelter where a Captain Poth would see him. The horseman gathered together his satchels and began his journey along the duckboards. A passing point was reached after about 300 yards, due to the manic activity: it was full with men awaiting their turn walking the opposite way. Captain Poth was grim; his commanding officer dead along with other key staff. His pile of B 104-83 forms: 'Posted as missing.' Even worse, form B104-82A: 'No further news having been Received. Regretfully constrained to conclude that X is dead,' were ready for Transportation; he decided to stack them up, pending a vehicle going on to Furnes. Accepting a bundle of papers, plans and photographs from Trevelyn, he subsequently asked the horseman to wait outside for a while.

Eventually Captain Poth called Trevelyn back in, giving him battle results with future predictions — a rather disturbing account to be conveyed onto Furnes. It left the lieutenant cold with fear. With no end in sight to the conflict, the privations experienced by most soldiers were manifest. Whole trains were used to transport munitions, but only wagons, (including horse drawn ones), carried away the wounded and injured, looked ominous. An increasingly large cycle of terror, escalating weekly, even daily, seemed to have a vice-like grip over everything. Somebody commented from the Roman Emperor Caligula's words: "Oderint dum metuant." "Let them hate, provided they are afraid." And many were.

The horseman left the trench in a nervous mood, remounted Morvah and slowly moved on from the encampments around Hooge. His best route back was to the outskirts of Ypres and away from the front towards Poperinge. The noise of shelling resonated as he overtook Red Cross wagons and lines of wounded men whenever possible. He too was overtaken by vehicles, empty now of supplies, carrying men catching a ride westwards. Further on, supply vehicles arriving from Furnes and points west were filling the oncoming road a lot of the time. All around him were destroyed wagons and trees, puddles and mud, rendering the sides of the fields and verges impossible for efficient riding.

Once again the smell of putrescent horses rent the air. The sight upset the stockman more than a little. His entire upbringing taught husbandry, care of, love of, animals. Seeing these creatures who only responded to commands ingrained in them by man, then destroyed by man was truly upsetting. He passed another windmill; so few were now left standing. It had been hit at around 15 feet from the ground and fell on its sails. Another very sad sight.

When the madness of this conflict had ended how on earth would economic activity be able to resume? There was nothing left! It was raining again and making progress on the slurry laden road was difficult. Colonel Fortescue had said use the countryside, he was not therefore bound by the larger roads. It was impossible to hack across fields due to their condition but Trevelyn resolved to find a track and begin a journey that would require cautious navigation but without the encumbrance of so much other traffic and debris. By tracking south he anticipated finding a building to stay the night in. Poperinge was a railhead, known by everyone as 'Pop'. With many railway wagons there, at worst he could sleep in an empty one; or at best the Skindles Hotel around the Grand Place might have a bed and a stable.

Finding a narrow road leaving the busy 'Pop' road he bore west, north west, then over a canal. He wanted to turn south but an opportunity did not arise immediately; never mind one soon would. The soldier was quite wet now and had been wearing wet or at least damp clothes since not long after leaving Furnes. It made his load heavier and the need for hot food ever more vital. He was very aware of the battle that was still raging to the east and wanted to find the least cluttered route back. It seemed to make sense especially as Colonel Fortescue had emphasized using the countryside.

Unfortunately Trevelyn did not find a way south to Poperinge and was continuing west as light failed. Cutting across fields would ruin the horse's legs; mud and puddles would inevitably suck the animal down, pull muscles and damage hooves. He made a decision that was not easy to take. There, on the flatlands of Flanders he would have to camp, but not under the stars for they were invisible. Within his backpack was a canvas, rolled up. He created a tent from it, a very uncomfortable tent but sufficient to keep off the gentle rain, and protect the satchels. Food, or the lack of it was a problem. He had a tin of bully beef, (corned beef) and digestive biscuits, and water within his canvas bottle. Uninspiring fayre yet better perhaps than that enjoyed by the horse, who made the best of rather indifferent grass by the side of the track. A puddle had to provide a drink for the beast.

An unsatisfactory ending to quite a difficult day. However, neither had any conception of what was to follow.

Having settled Morvah down and fallen asleep the soldier awoke to the noise of heavy rain upon the canvas, with rivulets trickling down his back, inside his collar. His body and his clothes were becoming sodden. Quite simply he felt wretched, with no more food left, only water. He needed to make his way to Furnes quickly, dry himself off and obtain hot food. The horse was none too happy either. Lack of good quality food reduced his energy levels and strength.

Sometime in the night the pair found themselves walking through the rain, north, in the general direction of the River Yser and towards Roesbrugge-Haringe. However, Trevelyn was aware that he had awoken with a cold. Hardly surprising, but it somehow dulled his perceptions a little.

Dawn came and progress was slow, the horse clearly had little energy and even less inclination to move. His head would drop involuntarily as though too heavy to hold up. Trevelyn spoke gently and continually encouraged his friend to go on. As the morning progressed the yeoman realised that he was developing a sore throat. Speaking became harder, his throat was sharp, swallowing increasingly difficult. Later he became aware of a light-headed feeling. Every now and again his head would momentarily seem to leave him. His hands were very cold. Inside his clothes his chest and torso burned. Later he was cold.

Losing all sense of time he just balanced himself correctly upon the horse by instinct, and made forward-going body movements. He had lowered his stirrups to almost the extent of his legs to make it easier for him to grip the horse, and his circulation seemed to benefit. Pins and needles were less regular as he was bearing down upon the stirrups with a larger area of his foot. Any pressure reduction was of assistance.

In time the now bedraggled pair reached the River Yser. The track led to a bridge, a very narrow one used for farm purposes only. Slowly though Trevelyn realized that the bridge was no longer whole. It had taken a shell from perhaps an air raid. He dismounted and inspected the condition of the bridge. It was safe for neither man nor beast. Through the haze of his feverish state, shivering, frightened, alone and still with a mission he slowly worked out that he had no alternative but to swim across the River

Yser, pulling Morvah along after him. If he slung the saddle bags and satchels across the water to the other bank, his backpack and boots too, he could take the horse's reins in one hand and swim, leading his precious mount to safety.

The solder knew that he would struggle with every part of the plan, due to physical weakness. He therefore decided to rest up for a while. The rain had stopped. He just needed to gain his strength, mental together with physical. Following an indeterminate time the yeoman enacted his plan. He managed to throw everything across the river. His socks were pushed into his boots, his helmet tied within his rucksack, coat, trousers and tunic too. The bags flew easily across the watery divide and clung to the bank on the other side. Now wearing just his undergarments, shirt and mittens, shivering he walked nervously, slowly down the bank, holding the reins in front of Morvah.

The horse did not want to move. For some reason he seemed to lean back. Trevelyn talked gently to the horse, pulling harder and harder. He was desperate to get this task over with; his own condition deteriorating all the time. Eventually the horse moved. Clearly the rapport between the two gave confidence to the animal. Then the soldier was out of his standing depth and began swimming whilst finally managing to encourage the animal into the water. The horse just sank and began to move downstream with the current. Trevelyn became aware that he was now midstream, but travelling with the river, not across it.

Terror struck him as he realised that his magnificent horse, trained and nurtured by him for eight years was not actually swimming. He had no strength left within his four legs. His head lifted as his body sank; his nose protruded from the water as he made grunting and snorting noises. Then Trevelyn realised that the sinking horse was pulling him down into the river as well as along it. He had a very quick, terrible decision to make. In order to save his own life he let go of the reins and swam as hard as his tired body would allow, heading for the bank. Glancing to his side at one moment he glimpsed the horse's nostrils for the last time; as they disappeared under the water, a few bubbles burst upon the surface.

Trevelyn scrambled to the far side, clawed his way up the bank, running 20 yards or so back along the bank to where his boots and clothing lay. Dressing as quickly as his befuddled head would allow he desperately croaked, "Morvah, Morvah," as he followed the trail of the river looking frantically for his precious friend. However there was no sign of the horse; he had clearly been totally exhausted, and perhaps affected by nerves from the earlier shelling, had drowned.

The soldier fell back on to the bank, then buried his head in his hands. Through his feverish condition he saw his friend walking, trotting, cantering and galloping across the Cornish fields. Green fields down to the River Fal, River Kenwyn, and Truro River. He saw the horse in his stable, kicking the lower partitioned door as he sensed the rider emerging to feed him in the morning. The enthusiasm of the horse, his spirit, zest for a canter when others would only trot, his kind eye, his good stable manners when being re-shoed, mucked out and groomed. All of that unique rapport that this particular man and beast found intuitive was gone. The Germans had some answers to provide for this, really they did.

Complete exhaustion now hit him very hard indeed. His limbs ached; he was sweating, yet cold and very, very tired. Gathering up his belongings, the backpack, satchels and pannier-type bags carried by the horse, perhaps 20 pounds in total, he wearily made his way straight ahead. Rather than try to discover Roesbrugge-Haringe he wanted to get to a road and find transport, any form of transport. His progress was extraordinarily slow. Now short of water, he was also facing a situation where another day could draw to a close without him being dry and fed. He knew that there were dangers to this. With a temperature, feverishness, light-headed feelings and other developing symptoms. Even this particular lone horseman experienced moments of needing and asking for help. Yet who from? His father was a long way away.

Trevelyn stumbled across the flatlands, almost unaware of time and his whereabouts; only will power and determination drove him on, with a sixth sense urging him forward to safety. If he collapsed it could mean the end of him; no one would ever know where exactly he had disappeared. With thousands of men disappearing in the trenches one yeoman sinking into a polder would barely rate a statistic.

Was he seeing a mirage through his developing fever? For at some indeterminate distance ahead a ridge appeared to form the impression of a road. He pushed on, breathing hard, sweating, panting, hot then cold, his every joint aching. It was a road; there was a country road ahead; he speeded up dragging the load, his heart beating so loud it seemed that everyone in the vicinity must be able to hear it. The landscape was devoid of people though. About 100 yards before the road he paused, tried to regulate his breathing, cleared perspiration away from his face and stood upright, aware that he had bent forward and constrained his respiration. The thought of a bath with a long hot soak passed through his mind as the light was now fading. Dragging himself the last few yards he saw a road crossing his view from left to right; a grass triangle and another village road going away from the triangle ahead. Looking around he tried to ascertain whether or not to turn right or walk straight on; both should reach Furnes but which was the busier road?

He turned around, the light-headed feeling overcame him and he collapsed in a heap on to the verge where he partly lay over a satchel, the sight resembling a sack of potatoes. As his mind drifted he was sufficiently non compis mentis to realise the severe difficulty that he now faced. Death was perhaps stalking him. He realized it was unlikely now that he would achieve his own dreams: those aspirations to farm in his own right, of making a name for himself, breeding then selling stock. His father would have no son, grandson, or progeny of his son, to carry on his own hard work. He would never take a wife, or experience that unique love betwixt man and woman which brought forth children. He sensed that this was his last season as he quickly began to lose consciousness while hallucinating.

CHAPTER IV

The military truck driver was singing, together with his four colleagues, as they bumped along the country road. Having left Poperinge, bound for Furnes, they had a decision to make concerning their route. Oostvleteren and up to Furnes was very busy. Unloading from the railway junction, cargo was usually transported upon this route; however a quieter route was to Roesbrugge-Heringe, crossing the River Yser following the road onwards towards Lo, turning left to Furnes just before the village.

So it was that a small convoy of six vehicles trundled its way through the morning mist and damp. They had full stomachs from the breakfast table, a happy disposition born out of a shared sense of security and being a few miles behind the trench line. Approaching the left junction, which would take them over the Belgian border and into France, thence to a village named Hondschoote thus keeping themselves away from the front, someone shouted: "Stop! Stop quickly, stop!" The front vehicle braked, and the following vehicles hooted, not understanding why in the middle of nowhere they needed to pause. A driver in another vehicle leaned out of his window and called, "What is wrong Harry, need a new washer?" referring to an unexpected call of nature. "No; look at this," came the reply. The first driver alighted from his cab, others were now joining him to surround the find. It was a British soldier; they rolled him onto his back. "'E's a gonner," said one. "Dreadful business," said another. Everyone seemed to have a phrase to sum up the situation.

The soldier's mouth and lips were parched dry, a white line of dried froth ran around the shape of his lips; his eyes rolled when opened and he was very cold. Someone had fetched a water bottle and pushed it into his mouth. Perhaps a drop trickled down his throat, much of it went over his chin and down his neck, though. They pulled out the identification tag, read it and discussed it. "Cornish Yeomanry. Then where is his horse?" asked one. "Galloped home if it has got any sense," quipped another. They looked inside his satchels, the panniers then his backpack, and decided to lay him in the back of a lorry with his property, take him to Furnes and the military hospital.

The formalities at Furnes for the convoy were short and sharp. Having driven in, one soldier took the panniers carried by Trevelyn to his regiment's senior duty officer, who in turn handed it to Colonel Fortescue's office. Meanwhile the yeoman himself was passed into the hands of the medics. The hospital facility was just outside the main encampment: a large old farmhouse, its dairy and buttery rooms being used for surgery, a church next door, damaged yet mostly water tight had been commandeered for a ward. All seating had been removed, its nave, chancel and side aisles had soldiers laying on either stretchers or straw mattresses side-by- side. The altar area had a desk, benches and surfaces used for administration with duty staff gaining an overview of those under their care. A small cloister used for exercise and sitting outside, weather permitting, the chapter house had become a laundry and kitchens, upstairs; were bunked down, the medical staff.

Into this desperate situation where men were fighting not a war but a battle for their own lives, arrived the Cornishman. An unfamiliar situation. Trevelyn was completely unaware of what was happening around him. Given just a cursory examination initially as there was no blood pumping from his body, nothing appeared missing, and he was not moaning; the doctor had many others who were obviously more in need of attention therefore he moved on to the next body.

Subsequently however, as time permitted a more detailed look was taken at the comatose soldier. A high temperature and feverish state were noted. His upper respiratory infections were either tonsillitis or pharyngitis. The clinical manifestations were evidently an onset of pain, swelling and stiffness in certain joints, profuse sweating, a rapid heart beat, and he was patently very tired, in fact physically exhausted. A decision was made to evacuate the man to a much bigger facility in Dunkirk. The field hospital was inappropriate for his needs, being not straightforward injuries to his person. A tag was hung around his neck 'For evacuation'.

Trevelyn was placed upon a stretcher then onto a bunk within a British Royal Army Medical Corps ambulance. The driver, unknown to the yeoman soldier, who was in and out of consciousness, was a young lady of his own age. A volunteer from a non-combatant country, in this case the United States of America. A pretty girl, well bred, well turned out, she would drive the six men in the Red Cross vehicle the short distance over to the border with France, to Dunkirk.

Later that day Trevelyn was wrapped in very heavy coarse brown army blankets in Dunkirk Hospital; the fever was intensifying, clearly he would need a period of convalescence. However there was insufficient room for him due to the sheer number of physically injured soldiery coming back from the front lines. As he was not bleeding or a needing to lie still following an operation, the notice 'For Evacuation' was placed on him again.

The young man was removed to the medical bay of a ship returning to Harwich. Unaware of returning to British soil, he tossed, turned, sweated, and slept for long periods. He was however acutely aware of his painful joints and unaccustomed stiffness, as he emerged from sleep, then turned and fell back into a deep sleep again.

The hospital facility in Harwich was overstretched and the staff were mostly interested in blood, snot and gore, whereas Trevelyn needed conventional bed care nursing. Regular changes of bedding too, having sweated the previous lot into a smelly damp heap. Also essential was regular turning of his body to avoid bed sores, along with lots of water, and gruel. Harwich authorities quickly decided that Trevelyn was not for them and placed him in an ambulance travelling to another hospital which was thought to be under far less pressure, being further away from the continent and British military activity.

Addenbrookes Hospital, Cambridge, admitted Trevelyn, along with many others needing medical treatment. Sadly oblivious to the beautiful city he was staying in, only a few yards from 'The Backs' with the profusion of flowers offering their annual display; also Kings College Chapel, with the anthems of Tomas Tallis, William Byrd, and Giovanni Palestrina filling the air. The musical canon by Tallis: 'Miserere Nostri' was indeed an entirely different type of canon to the ones recently heard by Trevelyn. He would not enjoy punting on the River Cam during this particular visit however.

A couple of days later the incoming wounded backing up from the now second battle of Ypres, and Belgium generally, was so great that again surgery cases were given beds closest to the European action. This fact meant that unfortunately Trevelyn and non-surgical cases had to be moved further west to minimise the movement of those who had received invasive surgical treatment. Once again oblivious to what was happening, now very ill, the soldier was driven in an ambulance to Nottingham Hospital. Upon arrival he was placed on a ward and left, then spotted by a nurse, who invoked the chain of command upwards until the ward sister attended to him. A doctor was immediately called who thoroughly examined the patient, talking through his procedure as he went about his examination, announcing, "Rheumatic fever." He then spoke aside to the sister, without the other more junior staff hearing.

The nursing staff cared for the yeoman soldier as attentively as they could but he seemed to make little progress. His response was ever more sleep, until the staff were concerned that he was slipping away from them.

The loss of the men who were incapacitated in one way or another was enormous. It was therefore not a shock for the recovering soldiery to see their colleagues moved from the ward to the mortuary at all times of day and night.

Around breakfast time concern was raised again regarding Trevelyn, then whilst the majority of the ward were still eating, a doctor was called. Pressed for time, quickly using his stethoscope upon the soldier's chest, he listened to Trevelyn's heart; given all of the previously accumulated knowledge about this patient he was prepared to rapidly pronounce death, and move onto the next case. There was pressure on the ward to free-up more beds, so a stretcher was called for, the recently pronounced 'dead' person was then rolled onto it.

Due to the mortuary overflowing a temporary resting place was found where bodies were laid; perhaps 15 recently deceased. Patients were placed outside the building on the grass, alongside a wall. They were in a straight line, head by the wall, feet by a path in a shady corner that never caught the sun. Orderlies were dispatched to find a tarpaulin with which to cover the bodies until the mortuary could receive more of them. Sadly, the backlog was due to relatives from all over the country having to journey to Nottingham to collect their loved ones. A nurse placed a label around the right wrist of Trevelyn describing who, what, where, and when, then left the sad patch of soil. The orderlies would soon appear with a tarpaulin to thus provide discretion for those whose lives had been cut short by another round of European conflict.

CHAPTER V

Creetown, Kircubrightshire — 1908

Andrew McNiven was reluctantly packing up and moving from the west of Scotland. Two generations previously his grandfather had left the Isle of Skye. Family legend backed by anecdote related that it had imperceptibly broken his heart, but financial constraints, the responsibility of a pregnant wife, along with career opportunities forced the change. So it was that his eldest son had stayed in the south west of Scotland, that equable environment where the Atlantic Drift or Gulf Stream meets the coast line and land mass. The climate gives forth palm trees, yuccas and other vegetation generally more associated with warmer climates, the Mediterranean even. Frost and snow were not on the agenda for local weather forecast options. They were other people's worries. Now however the third generation living on the mainland had to face the enduring problem of the Celt, that hardy breed of the western edges of Britain, due to work and income pressures; he must often accept leaving hallowed turf.

He had worked very hard from scratch to build a unique business. Travelling the highlands and islands during the times of year when the tides and weather permitted buying cloth: tartans, tweeds, worsteds, wools — any and all garments that he believed would sell on the mainland. By bringing the traditional materials and garments of old Scotland to primarily an English market, he satisfied the desire for not only fine merchandise, but very practical and warm clothing. His customers were variously retailers of male or female garments, haberdashery businesses. Travelling salesmen also bought from him, they then journeyed around the country areas and towns knocking upon doors to sell the products. However travellers were less easy to deal with due to their seemingly acute cash flow problems. Shops and market tradesmen were apparently easier to trade with.

Now, with the great urban populations demanding ever more choice from their shops the demand upon McNiven to select, buy, store, transport and supply, with repeat orders if a particular line was retailing well, had become all-consuming. The railway system was central to quickly expediting orders. Further, commissioning of a particular line that fashion dictated as popular was important, yet a very subjective area.

Storage facilities were crucial, and sadly the facilities that he needed to grow the business, (and perhaps leave to his two sons), were no longer in Creetown. The little old town made its income from granite quarries: blocks of granite that had built Lancashire towns, including Liverpool and Merseyside. It looked across to Wigtown and its bay. Behind the town were truly beautiful hills and forests.

Yet despite the pull of Celtic ancestry, using language such as is spoken in the marriage ceremony: "That mystical union betwixt man and woman," the mystical union between himself and his immediate country would sadly be unable to hold him, simply because of the need to progress the business for his family. The spell would still bind him though and the regular long trips from England into the highlands and islands between May and September would have to replenish the urge to wander mountain and valley, to drink in the sight of lochs, to smell the air of island, heather and forest, to converse about the culture, whilst sharing a dram.

He had taken back his own drinking vessel from the Ellangowan Hotel on St John Street. The Saturday evening privilege of discourse and humour with his own kind, old Nathaniel MacTavish reciting the words of Robert Burns. The bard would almost inevitably be invoked, as old Mac supped deeply. 'The Lass of Cessnock Banks', 'Mary Morison', 'Montgomery's Peggy' and 'Duncan Gray' who went to woo; all made him think of his dear wife and mother of his three daughters and two sons. Indeed Robbie stirred a certain emotion in a man proud of his cultural inheritance. Awareness of one's broad cultural background is essential in the building of a real man. Being part of the Celtic diaspora may dilute his immediate experience, but not the memory. Yet he recalled the English had a writer who like Robbie could create a verse from any subject. Rudyard Kipling, in 'The Reeds of Runnymede' his exultation of Magna Carta, the charter whose concepts were given by the British to the world. 'Heritage', and 'The Nature Born', whose eulogies are appropriate when song, dance and word were interwoven sometimes with a dram, and during a naturally patriotic shared invocation of literary experience. Perhaps the future was not so barren after all!

The businessman had built three houses, north of Nottingham, close enough to the main railway line and good roads serving the larger populations. He had designed storage facilities and had already transported his wares, his stock in trade, then hired staff who would hopefully prove suitable for the endeavour. He was now completing his move by transporting his wife, family, and worldly chattels to the new home. The remnants of the Creetown business together with all household items, seven humans and two cats were loaded. One particularly independent cat chose to remain, taking off to a neighbour during the packing. Cats have their own ways of choosing their lifestyle and company. The lorries were ready to leave, saying goodbye to neighbours was slowly accomplished. The town clock built for Queen Victoria's Silver Jubilee in 1897 said 12:20.

Customers were entering the Hotel Ellangowen as the convoy passed along St John Street and the brightly painted doors of the cottages, then the newer church built in 1834. The original Kirkmacbreck Church was way up on the left towards the fell, probably abandoned around 1645; only sheep and cattle that now visited that original churchyard saw the crumbling structure and fallen gravestones. Now from somewhere above them, conveyed by the breeze, the sound of someone practicing the bagpipes; the sound wafted, perhaps young McIvor ordered from the house, by his family, wishing for peace, or at least with their neighbours. It had the effect of a lament, rather than a fond farewell.

Many locals had turned out to wave the family a cheery goodbye. It was however tinged with sadness, as Celts always worry about the emptying of their homeland. Further, the internal combustion engine was noticeably emptying the villages and smaller town communities of their men folk during working hours; leaving, in a sense, dormitories. This was a process that favoured large combines in business whilst disadvantaging the small enterprise. There was already a reduction in bakeries and small breweries as a lorry or dray could swiftly deliver to one retailer then on to the next one. People questioned their own future. Now yet another family was taking flight.

The McNiven family arrived at their arranged destination as a unit, but already the family were dispersing like September Martens (birds). Fiona had been accepted at University College Hospital in London to train as a nurse; her younger sister Iona proposed the same career path; another daughter favoured being a couturier as a compliment to her father's business; one son was undecided, the other was looking at tailoring.

Business quickly prospered for McNiven; his strategy for its development proved instantly right. The fine merchandise from Scotland was much sought after; hunting and shooting people bought it, practical people needing warmth and durability bought it. There were ever more families opening up retail shops to complement tailoring, thus fabrics, together with finished garments, sold to both men and women. The Victorian industrial class had produced a breed of man who could afford to clothe his wife and himself with less concern for the pennies. His offspring then aspired to the same, if not better.

McNiven worked hard, travelled far and made contracts all over the country. He missed his home though, as the necessity for expeditions into western Scotland took much time. His staff were permitted to visit his customers once accounts were arranged, but it was his own intuition that made the right purchases at the right time, commissioned the required materials that would actually sell and not languish within his stores, thus depleting cash flow. He stayed in many hotels, and mostly knew the good from the bad or indifferent. Costs of such journeys were vital to keep 'within bounds' and he therefore saved money by selecting cheaper lodging upon occasions.

Transportation costs from the islands further eroded profit; bad weather could delay a shipment, potentially causing a missed deadline on the mainland. On one such trip, in an effort to cut outgoings McNiven stayed in a lesser hotel for a couple of nights. The facilities were adequate, although running water proved rather spasmodic, almost as though reluctant to flow. Perhaps there was a burst pipe somewhere nearby causing a loss of pressure. At the hotel he ate local water cress together with other raw vegetables. Initially he felt just unwell with rather unspecific symptoms. Deciding to visit a doctor, unusual for him, he was advised that his small intestine was swollen, quite clearly inflamed along its length. He endured a rather uncomfortable journey south by which time his intestine had ulcerated. The ulcers perforated then bled. Five days later, by now in Nottingham Hospital he died, through loss of blood caused by perforated ulcers. Several others staying at the hotel had, it became evident suffered identical symptoms and also died from typhoid, in a typical localised outbreak.

With the death of her husband, his loving wife hired the services of a manager to oversee the business and maintain it. There was every reason to believe in its continuing success, other than worries concerning the purchasing element. However the business quickly went into lossmaking. Sadly the hired hand was defrauding the widow by systematically thieving money and stock. With neither son yet ready to assume control the widow sold out her remaining interests in McNiven's business and coped by living off the income from the two other houses that her husband had built.

*   *   *

Two daughters were now fully qualified nurses. The one who was based in Nottingham was posted to a casualty ward. With the onset of war it was anticipated, indeed expected, that the provincial hospital would receive extra patients from the eastern towns and cities as casualties were brought home. Miss Iona McNiven was living in nurse's accommodation during her working week, then catching the train home at weekends, or for her days off . A working routine evolved that was also a very interesting learning curve. Further, she was able to share her experiences with Fiona, her sister in London. They wrote regularly. Fiona was now developing a broad and varied social life, beginning to travel, including abroad. Every spare hour was a whirlwind of theatres, museums, galleries, and dates. There was about her an element of the bohemian now. What would father have said? Did mother even know? However, if mother knew about her radical thought processes there would be a proper row!

CHAPTER VI

Morning duties for Nurse McNiven involved picking up where the previous day had ended, looking at the records of the patients, turning those who were in bed long term, to prevent sores. The routine of bed care. Then sister's initial checks before matron's rounds; each occurred daily. The surgeon would visit too. Having dressed for duty and attended Francis Drake Ward, Miss NcNiven placed her private possessions, in this instance just a handbag and pair of more feminine shoes, into her locker within the staff room.

Walking the ward, the staff nurse approached McNiven and a colleague, then advised that many soldiers had arrived overnight. Sadly a dozen or so were not destined to see daybreak and had died through the night, others since. As the mortuary was already full, certain bodies had been laid upon the grass outside the building. The young nurses were told that they should take bodies to this place if any new deaths occurred on the ward during that morning. They would be informed as and when the mortuary could accept more bodies. Naturally the lassies were saddened by what they heard. It caused quite a stir with the staff. Discussions about lives cut short, wasted, families heartbroken, were inevitable.

It was not permissible for nurses to leave their wards without authorisation. Even a journey to the toilet was frowned upon. "Why couldn't this not be arranged before duty, or during a break?' they were asked. The early morning break arrived; time for a drink. Nurse McNiven had experienced melancholy, mainly due to the news of the deaths of so many young men. She now felt a need to visit the bodies outside and pay her respects. As she left the building two orderlies were unfolding a tarpaulin, checking its size and refolding it.

The nurse approached the line of dead soldiers, some wearing their uniforms still, others in hospital pyjamas. A desperate sense of foreboding overcame her. Tears welled up, she gulped hard. Walking the line of young men, she counted 15. Some clean shaven; with the marbling effect to the skin following death they seemed even younger. Too young to die anyway.

She looked at name tags: regiment, date of birth. At the end of the line she paused, in prayer, and slowly began her return journey down the line. Stopping, looking at one young face, drawing her eyes down to his chest, she thought that she noticed it move. Clearing her head by looking away she then fixed her eye once again upon the young man, again she saw an almost imperceptible movement of his chest. Her knees buckled, touching underneath her uniform and petticoats.

She first clasped her head with both open hands, then clapped them together; they were now sweating. Her mouth opened wide, together with her eyes; she tried to cry out. Nothing happened. Thinking quickly she knelt down to look at the name tag: 'Edwin Trevelyn, Cornish Yeomanry. Transferred to Royal Horse Artillery. Date of Birth: 21.06.90 Truro.' The nurse began running around the building to an external door as the orderlies were making their way towards the corner of the building carrying a suitable tarpaulin.

"No!" she called putting up a hand, "No, no, no!" The bemused men stopped in their tracks and looked at one another.

The nurse ran quickly to her locker, grabbed at her handbag, rifling around she found her vanity mirror, turned, and running with it shouted out for everyone to hear: "He's alive, he's alive!" and left colleagues looking stunned. Returning to the bodies, where by now the orderlies had arrived to provide reasonable privacy, she placed the small mirror under the soldier's nose. For perhaps half a minute she watched the glass, until utterly convinced that the corpse was not a corpse. By now others had arrived: nurses, and a doctor. The glass clearly had condensation upon it. There was breathing; he was, incredibly, alive. A terrible mistake had been made. Someone called for a stretcher. The soldier was returned to a ward, suddenly a plethora of hospital staff buzzed around wanting to assist.

Iona McNiven put in a request to the ward sister to have specific responsibility for Trevelyn. When on duty she would nurse him. Barely alive, the soldier was actually very unlikely to survive. His very faint heart beat was rapid, his joints were swollen, a stiffness in them resembling rigour mortis. It was uncertain whether or not he was sufficiently nourished to have enough physical strength. In his favour however he was very fit, agile, determined and bright. His positive attributes were all in place to assist in the fight for life.

The required nursing was largely bed care and highly nutritious food, plenty of liquid. As he was consistently just lying in bed, regular turning reduced the chance of bed sores. His fever caused excessive sweating, necessitating changes of sheets. Quite oblivious to all that was happening around him Trevelyn spent several days in deep sleep, feverish, just waking to turn. His pyjamas were changed several times daily, sheets too when he was sponge washed as well. One day the soldier was emerging from sleep, his mouth and tongue moving as though salivating, his eyes rolled. On duty, Nurse McNiven saw movement within the bed and went over. She was looking down upon the young man with a gentle motherly smile, her large eyes wide open.

The soldier seemed to look into them but did not focus upon her. She wiped his face with a damp cloth. His eyes rolled then slowly began to focus, his mouth opened, perhaps trying to formulate words. This was the beginning only, of emerging from a terrible fever, recovering from intense cold and excessive travel. Having looked carefully at one another, the nurse patted one of his hands, placed it within the sheets, raised her eyebrows, smiled and said, "Aye, you will survive laddie; keep fighting," then slowly moved onto another patient, as he fell asleep again.

As the days passed Trevelyn gradually took more interest in his surroundings. He had little chats with Nurse McNiven, which she was often forced to curtail as the staff nurse, or even worse sister, might observe them. She was fearful of anyone observing their rapport; fraternisation was frowned upon. The nurse was rather chuffed at her efforts to save a life. Now sitting up, her special patient was treated to a gift. One day she drew the curtains around Trevelyn's bed and slipped to him some fresh bread and cakes that she and her mother had baked. The young man was overjoyed, special treatment, and from such a bonnie girl!

Then, mail began to arrive from Truro. The family had been given details of their son's whereabouts and were sending letters and packages. A large parcel of brawn, haslet, Cornish clotted cream and chocolate allowed the soldier to share his booty with his colleagues. Something to gamble with when card games were played as well! The news from Cornwall was very exciting. Agnes had just married; they were farming near to St Trevor in the Penzance area. Life was tough, money was short but George Provins came from hard working stock; they would make out.

Father could occasionally take the train to Penzance and advise upon cattle problems, a reassurance for a young man to have an older, experienced head available.

Martha, engaged, was planning her wedding to the son of a local businessman. She had come first in an important dressage competition held near Exeter. The farmer had inculcated into his progeny great respect for, love of and an ability to work with animals. This was to him a reward. Charlotte, the extrovert, a demonstrative character was 'walking out' with a young man who was, yes, a guards officer. She had taken him to chapel, to concerts, to the farm for lunch, tea, dinner and any other meal she could think of. Ever the show lady she wanted everyone to see him with her. His family had a rubber plantation somewhere in Burma. It mattered little. What mattered to Charlotte was that she was seen with this handsome man in his dress uniform. Everything would flow from there, apparently. Many people from chapel were mentioned, there was a list of eligible young ladies wanting to visit the farm in order to take tea with Edwin. His choice of a wife was to be made easy, and evidently quickly, upon his return home. News was passed on about school friends, the Farmers' Club people, and traders around the city. Father enclosed a copy of the Holy Bible with many references for scholarly reading. Matthew 6:34: 'Do not be anxious, God will take care of your tomorrow, live one day at a time,' was but one offering. Father always knew how to invoke the Bible, more especially when he sought to chastise though.

A visit was being arranged. Father and Charlotte would catch a train, perhaps to Paddington, then up to Nottingham. Their recovering relative would hear in due course. Having time upon his hands allowed Trevelyn the unusual opportunity to write on a regular basis to everyone. He tried to express his uncertainty about the so-called eligible girls from the chapel though. They were not, well, exactly his type of girls. Evidently, father would hear none of it. Hitherto unknown talents were attributed to girls who Trevelyn had previously dismissed as plain bores.

One morning after breakfast the ward sister spoke with Trevelyn and instructed him to attend her office at 1400 hours. Representatives from the army were to visit him. Having received a parcel from home of smart clothes, he shaved, dressed in lovat green cavalry twill trousers, waistcoat and a tweed jacket with brogues. The epitome of a Cornish country gentleman. Representing the army were two officers of different generations. The older one spoke and explained the situation; whilst the younger one seemed programmed to nod, smile and agree with everything said by the older man. They were courteous, factual and businesslike, thanking Trevelyn for his war efforts. He had shown considerable bravery, physical and mental endurance. The satchels and pannier type bags had all been returned with usable contents.

They were very sorry indeed for the young officer's condition but had to bring the sad news that following medical reports he was now physically unfit for any further military service. There could never be any criticism regarding his efforts; he had carried out his duties as ordered, but his physical health must be his prime concern now. It was a sad moment. Trevelyn was worried that he had let the side down. No he had not. He enquired about Morvah. No mention had been made by anyone concerning his horse. It saddened him greatly that his magnificent beast who had responded so assiduously to training, lunging, jumping, hacking out and exhibited such exemplary manners within his stable, was gone forever. He would have to start all over again. Finding such a creature with the right potential was the difficult part.

The army officers stood, saluted their former colleague, then shook his hand warmly and said their 'thank you's'. At which point sister, who was not hitherto visible, providentially appeared in the room. She squeezed one of Trevelyn's elbows, thanked everyone and offered to show the army men out. Trevelyn was invited to spend the rest of the day on the balcony in social pursuits with other patients. He slowly walked out of the room, along a corridor and into the ward, where Nurse McNiven turned to catch his glance. He approached her, told her of his lot, mentioning the sad story of Morvah. She tried to lighten his mood. He was clearly susceptible to her manner. The nurse had to be aware of staff nurse and sister, who would scold her if they suspected any over familiarity. Indeed jealous colleagues might just tell a tale. Clearly everyone appreciated that a certain rapport would develop between two human beings where one had directly saved another's life. This particular situation would be enhanced due to the bravery of the young man, beauty of the woman, and eligibility of both individuals .

Days passed, which saw Trevelyn gradually build his physical strength. As the fever left him he had begun eating a full meal every time. Having lost around two stones in weight and experienced muscle wastage due to lying in bed he was encouraged to eat and drink as much as he could manage. Then plenty of rest with bed care. His sleeping patterns normalized as his body recovered. As his body and mind changed through the recovery so did his sense of fun, and a natural playfulness returned. It was quite usual in these circumstances for young men in particular to enjoy teasing the young nurses, the higher ranking nurses maintain decorum, especially when matron is around, or a surgeon's visit imminent. Practical joking, gentle verbal jesting is all part of extended stays in hospital.

Trevelyn enjoyed teasing and tormenting Nurse McNiven; she had the ultimate response though of sending him back outside for more fresh air! He shared with her food sent from the farm. She found numerous reasons to attend to him, or walked close past his bed in order to elicit a tease, or a jibe about something. One day sister called McNiven into her office and drew to her attention the unacceptable amount of time that she was spending with a particular patient, and that it was being remarked upon . She did not in any way condemn the nurse, just a warning to be careful and not make it so obvious. The older woman fully understood the natural inclinations of young and eligible people, but had to maintain discipline. There was a balance to strike, as with so many situations in life, she explained.

Nurses were allowed to walk out around the grounds with the patients, some assisting by pushing wheelchairs . Often several patients and their nurses would journey around the gardens on a fine day. Those who wished to smoke a cigarette or their pipe could do so outside. During one afternoon when a group of six or so went out walking Nurse McNiven was with them. At one point she was beside Trevelyn and allowed the back of her hand to brush along the back of his hand. When their eyes met just afterwards she gave him a look that he had never encountered before; it made him swallow hard, and his heartbeat sounded loud. He was ill equipped to respond immediately, being quite overcome with joy. Later he obliquely acknowledged the gesture; she responded with raised eyebrows. Now he knew that flirting was possible he continued to return the fun. Whenever he did she gave more back. No shrinking violet Miss

Iona McNiven; this lass was assertive, yet deeply shy as well. How strange. Trevelyn was certainly learning all the time.

One day a letter arrived from Truro. It announced the imminent visit of Mr Edward Trevelyn and Miss Charlotte Trevelyn. The stern Cornishman wanted to make sure that his only son was being properly cared for, together with ensuring that his spiritual welfare was being taken care of. He had brought yet another Holy Bible, within which he placed markers for study reference, to assist his son.

When the Cornish family arrived they were given dispensation to spend an entire day with their relative. Having travelled so far, with overnight stays necessary, Matron encouraged a longer than usual visit. It was good for morale. As things turned out Iona McNiven was not on duty for the duration of the visit; however her presence was felt as her role in saving the soldier's life was mentioned. Whenever the young man talked of her his father responded by speaking about girls from their local chapel. Charlotte boomed around the ward telling everyone what to do; there appeared endless opportunities for bossing!

The men spoke at length about cattle, existing stock, new stock, an impending trip to the Channel Islands to buy more cattle and the butcher's shop in Pydar Street which was trading well as the farm was able to fulfil customers' requirements. The biggest problem for Trevelyn Senior was finding a good shop manager. He had recently sacked one for theft: the man not only stole from the till, but was removing meat from the shop to sell off privately. A chance conversation with a woman in chapel revealed that the manager visited homes with parcels during the evenings. He was followed one evening and then confronted. Dreadful business, having to confront a man thus.

The younger man talked about his horse and the requirement to find another one. The rapport between the two men when talking about animals, farming and the land was spontaneous; they became lost in detail, of lessons from history, of others' experiences, good or bad. The livestock market provided a wealth of shared discussion too. When it came time to say goodbye the older man shook his son's hand, saying he would welcome him back as soon as was possible; there was much work to do. Charlotte flapped around causing her own style of mayhem; everyone was aware of who she was by now: they had all received advice of some sort.

Events surrounding the Trevelyn family lingered within the ward. Nurse McNiven questioned her colleagues, and more subtly the patients, in an attempt to build a picture of this unknown breed. Farming was a subject not fully appreciated by her; they were quite different from her family, though similarities existed. Her own father's quest for income had been precarious upon occasions, no salary cheque or wage packet for him unless he drove himself and the staff forward. The independent streak of the Celt was shared. Young Trevelyn had about him the air of 'Praise the Lord and pass the bullets,' — determination, all gung ho! She liked that. His father clearly had that a generation previously, otherwise his enterprise would never had prospered.

The general surgeon and a junior doctor visited Trevelyn one morning whilst upon their rounds. They examined and questioned the young man at length. Satisfying themselves that he was ready to be dismissed from their care they warned him of the likely reoccurrence of the disease and told him to write home immediately, as he would be released the following week. The letter home elicited an instant reply, he would be met at Truro station by one or two of his sisters. His room was ready; everyone, the staff, neighbours, chapel people, literally everyone was ready to welcome him home.

During her last shift before Trevelyn left, Nurse McNiven found a medical reason to draw the curtains around his bed. She administered to the sheets, plumped up the pillows and frankly did a lot of very little. Reaching across the bed for some reason, she very slowly leaned over Trevelyn's head; pausing she gently kissed his forehead. Simultaneously she pressed in his hand a folded piece of paper. Then with the air of an efficient medical person she moved around quicker, drew back the curtain and went about her business.

Trevelyn was overcome. While opening the paper under the sheets a joker in a bed nearby questioned what he was doing. Laughter erupted all around, bringing the incident to the notice of the staff nurse, who wanted to know about what was going on. The piece of paper had an address written upon it with a three-inch length of girl's hair ribbon stuck to it. The young man was in such a flap he could not sleep, tossing and turning he drew attention to himself as the duty night nurse walked over to enquire about his problem.

The following day Trevelyn prepared to leave for Nottingham Station. He was to travel in a hospital wagon along with others; destination London St Pancras, then crossing the capital to Paddington for the Penzance train, alighting at Truro. His goodbyes were extensive, given the duration of his stay. Handshakes all around the ward, the kitchen, and other staff who had formed part of his recent life. He did not have the chance to spend much time with Nurse McNiven alone but found a stolen moment to press into her hand a piece of paper containing his own address, and a verse from William Shakespeare:

> 'Shall I compare these too a summer's day?
> Thou art more lovely and more temperate:
> Rough winds do shake the darling buds of May
> And summers lease hath all too short a date.'

It was only a glance that allowed them to acknowledge their parting, the general hubbub followed by a sudden rush as the wagon arrived prevented him from doing something he was aching to do, kiss the lassie upon her cheek. A bitter sweet moment indeed.

CHAPTER VII

As the Great Western train slowed in its approach to the railway station arches Trevelyn stood up, and removed his property from the luggage racks. Looking over to his left he noticed the cathedral with its three spires, the chapel, and the confluence of the rivers Allen and Kenwyn into the Truro River. He glanced at the Coinage Hall where he had met up with the other Cornish lads. Whatever became of them? he thought. The train halted, puffed its last before staff began opening the doors. It was Martha who he saw first; she was dressed for riding. Then he spied Charlotte telling some hapless character what to do, or perhaps where to go! The girls were overjoyed as they hugged their younger brother.

Charlotte, unable to contain herself blurted out that Agnes was pregnant. "Hush," said Martha, "That's for later; not in public dear please." Outside the station Trevelyn had a surprise. Martha had brought 'Tilley', her dressage horse and requested her brother to ride it home; the girls would walk either side of him carrying his few belongings. As they passed people en route they called out and waved. Along Station Road, Treyew Road and into Green Lane they walked, then right onto the Falmouth Road, ultimately into the farm property around the old oak tree and down facing the river, to the farm. They sang "Ride on, ride on in majesty! Hark, all the tribes hosanna cry! O Saviour meek, pursue thy road with palms and scattered garments stowed." Charlotte called out, "Hark, we are the Cornish tribe." It was a hedonistic moment.

All of the farm staff turned out to greet him, neighbours were there too. The farmer looked on in pride as his son was eulogised. Further, there was much news, everyone wanted to have their say!

The following Sunday after chapel lunch was arranged, not only for the family, an eligible girl and her sister were invited too. After the meal everyone contrived to leave Edwin alone with Maud Polwithal. He was appalled. The hapless girl bore no resemblance to what the former soldier was looking for. After she and her sister had left, Trevelyn Senior called his son into the front room; standing with a thumb in his waistcoat he was earnest regarding his enquiry. "Well, what do you think? About Miss Polwithal I mean."

"Dull," was the reply. His father then questioned him in some detail concerning his intentions, and did not like what he heard.

The younger man explained that he wanted life in a girl, one with some go in her. His father replied that it was up to a man to train a wife, he could encourage the girl in the direction that he wanted. The younger man failed to impress his father with his explanation. He did not want to marry a chapel girl, further he had not met a girl in Truro that he was drawn to, well not yet anyway. The older man then listed off a number of his son's contemporaries from school in the area — for example, who were either engaged or actually married; they were happy.

There was an awkward silence which was broken by the older man very slowly walking over to his desk; opening a draw slowly he took out an envelope. Tapping it onto the palm of one hand he glared at his son.

"There was a letter delivered here earlier this week; it has a postmark from Nottingham. He paused for maximum effect. "No doubt from your flibberty jibbett nurse woman."

"She is not a flibberty jibbett father; she is a very well brought up lady from a good hard working family."

"There will be no good come of this my lad, no good at all" said the father.

"What is wrong with me seeing her, father?"

"I'll tell you what is wrong lad, she is not Cornish that is what is wrong lad."

The older man was shaking with rage, he was not used to being defied, his word was always the end of the matter. Walking away from his son to leave the room he handed a letter over. With contempt in his voice: "I suppose that you had better have this, as your name appears upon the envelope; you are Trevelyn Junior," he said, emphasizing the word "junior". " I warn you, no good can possibly come of this"

He left the room. Both parties were angry and sad; they were not destined to see eye-to-eye on this issue.

The letter was very stimulating. Full of news, family talk, a statement of 'missing you', some quotations and another small length of ribbon. Trevelyn set about replying to this exciting development. Charlotte realised how matters were developing. Her easy going open personality allowed her to become an intermediary. She tried to calm things down. Father was implacable though; his son was to marry a Cornish girl; there were plenty to choose from. In argument, Charlotte used as a case, the example of her beau having a plantation in Burma. Father said that was irrelevant, she was a girl.

A pattern developed whereby Trevelyn Senior provided a succession of what he considered suitable young ladies for his son to spend time with. The more he tried, the more frustrated he became with his son, and the more letters kept arriving from Nottinghamshire.

Then Martha married and left the farm; Charlotte too. Agnes had her second baby, another girl, leaving Trevelyn father and son together at the farm with the housekeeper Mary Lee. A telephone had been fitted before the war and young Trevelyn was able to make telephone calls, long distance to an arranged site. It was so very exciting. One morning after milking was complete and all stock fed, young Trevelyn washed and changed, then left the farm to walk into Truro. Upon his return his father was hovering, waiting to pounce upon his son and enquire about his mission.

"To have my photograph taken," was his reply.

"What?!" boomed his father cussing the anticipated usage of the image that was to be collected the following week.

During this particular exchange Mary Lee happened to mention that when she made the son's bed and cleaned his bedroom she could not help but notice the two photographs of a girl that now stood upon his chest of drawers. She commented upon the beauty of the girl, her fine features, and bright eye. After an awkward silence Trevelyn Senior said that his son had better fetch the photographs and allow him to view them, as they were in his house. His son ran upstairs as quickly as his legs would carry him; placing the pictures in front of his father he could not cease talking. He listed the girl's attributes, was verbose regarding her talents, looks, personality; and anyway she saved his life, he added.

His father just stared at the images; one of a nurse wearing full uniform, with her long hair tied neatly at the back of her head. The other, in which she was wearing a suit jacket, blouse and a set of pearls, was hand tinted by an artist in order to replicate true colours. The girl's hair was down. She had such a twinkle in her eye, such a smile, which could melt the hardest man. The farmer stared long and hard, almost in disbelief. His mind wandered as quite involuntarily a smile crossed his face as his senses discerned the emotionally overwhelming Clarinet Concerto by Wolfgang Mozart, the second movement resonated; it reflected the beauty of the images now before him. Gone for a fleeting moment was his resolve, composure and absolute control. He only said very quietly, "But she is not Cornish," and sighed. Giving the images back to his son he began to walk out of the room, then he turned slowly and said, "Son I think that you should write to Mrs McNiven, Iona's mother, inviting her daughter to spend her next annual leave at the farm. I need to investigate the situation."

The younger man jumped with joy; he thanked his father sincerely, beside himself with gratitude; once his father met the girl he would think differently.

Finally the dreadful Sunday lunches ceased. No more interview sessions with hapless creatures who attended in the belief that a romantic future may follow the coffee! The flow of letters increased to and from Nottinghamshire, telephone calls too. They made their arrangements by letter for each call; it was expensive to telephone long distance. Sometimes they had to wait for a connection. Very occasionally it was not possible to make a connection at all.

Mrs McNiven returned the letter of invitation for her daughter to spend her annual leave upon the farm, assenting to the young man's request. Arrangements were thus put in place for the summer of 1916.

After the winter had released its grip young Trevelyn applied himself to finding another horse. It was all very well riding other horses but training his own was a part of life. By the time of Iona's visit he would be in a position to show her what he was capable of. Cantering, galloping, jumping, how she would be impressed. Then at Truro livestock market one day a conversation about horses led to meeting a man from Feock who wanted to sell his three-year-old Anglo-Arab. Father and son visited the property of a Mr James Betournay who said little, just what was necessary to discuss.

Father Trevelyn turned to his son. "A still tongue makes a wise head. Remember your proverbs lad. This man is honest; he makes no effort to sell the horse; he is not hiding vices with clever words." They rode the horse, examined its teeth, legs and hooves in particular, its body in general. 'Poacher' was 16.2 hands; that is measurements of four inches corresponding to a man's hand when measured across his palm — the standard equine denotion of size. He had a white blaze down the front of his head, the rest of him was chestnut in colour. They were unable to discern any vices; on the contrary the horse appeared to have a generous spirit and was forward going. So the younger Trevelyn bought him after a short but amicable haggle over the price.

Poacher responded well to his new rider, worked hard when rounding up cattle, indeed he performed whenever asked to. His jumping was relaxed and stable manners were fine. No worries for the blacksmith here!

Life had resumed its earlier routine before the interruption by Germany. The farm was prosperous and successful due to sheer hard work, knowledge of animals and their husbandry. Working days were long, however with two men sharing a vested interest; the enterprise employing trusted staff as well, made it possible to have time off. The older man was very demanding though; an Old Testament character, he saw only a therapeutic aspect to work. Pleasure-seeking was not his forte; his life had dealt him severe blows. The loss of two wives in childbirth, which for a man of such instinctive religious beliefs left him pained inside, but he was unable to express it outside. Bringing up four children with a seven-day farming business was very hard going. This man had a survival instinct, with the belief in individual responsibility as expressed by Ezekiel the prophet. However he saw all around him the fulfilment of 'The Revelation' to John.

He was not an easy man to work with but scrupulous; his mid-Victorian upbringing had not equipped him for the world that was unfolding. Whilst he only meant well, wanted to do the right thing for, and to his fellow man, the value systems evolving as a result of the terrible war raging in Europe and beyond were confusing to him. The constitutional practices that had been taken all over the world by the British; practices that were sound, that gave hitherto unknown freedoms to people were now under attack at home. A radicalism with little or no basis other than a destructive godless envy was taking hold. It seemingly had no means to solve poverty or food queues, yet removed all concept of personal and individual responsibility, substituting the state. It denied God. It was not for Trevelyn.

Preparations were complete for the summer visitor; she would use Martha's room. Charlotte also wanted to visit from Lamorna and share time with Iona, therefore her bedroom was made ready too. Although the farm was destined to greet an important visitor, it still needed to maintain its routine; animals demanded their own daily rituals and routines.

Edwin met his young lady off the Cornish Riviera. A Great Western train puffed and pulled its beautiful maroon and cream carriages over the railway arches and into Truro station, where people, goods and chattels were then met or collected. The couple stared longingly at one another, almost uncertain, shook hands, then kissed upon the cheek.

Literally everything was new for the girl. The architecture, and accents of many people; they spoke much faster than many of her acquaintance. Smells were different too. The industrial Midlands, her home now, could be grimy, grey, heavy somehow. Certain of the smells and sounds were similar to Scotland though.

The young man eager to impress, by way of courtship had tacked up his father's pony, attached his trap and collected the lassie in style, treating her to a quick trip around his city, by way of Richmond Hill, Ferris Town and down to Boscowen Street, turning right up Lemon Street, with its magnificent Georgian architecture where properties are both kind to the eye and practical in use. Climbing the steep hill tested the pony with its burden. They passed the column displaying a memory of Richard Lander, that great explorer and map-maker of Africa. Their own short exploration of the beautiful old city needed no maps, just an enthusiastic guide.

Farming presented very many new sights, smells, activities; the girl's inclination to learn though was excited as tending and caring for cattle, sheep, pigs and horses was a new experience for the nurse. A new language was discernible; just as every trade or profession has its own language so does farming. A fine tilth did not refer to a soft material but to the working condition of a particular soil! The headland; not a skull, but the uncultivated edges of a field.

The housekeeper Mary Lee assisted Iona with unpacking. She explained the rhythms of farm life from the point of view from the kitchen. It had been decided to have a reception dinner for Iona that evening. Charlotte would be up from Lamorna later. Martha and her husband Percival Fitzwalter would visit too.

It was planned that Iona would be formally presented to Mr Edward Trevelyn at five o'clock in the afternoon, spend up to forty-five minutes alone talking with him; the others would then be called into the sitting room for perhaps a quarter of an hour before a six o'clock dinner. Edwin's sisters arrived early in order to assist both Mary Lee and Iona with preparations. The nurse's older sister Kathleen, the couturier, dress and other garment-maker had produced a very special creation for her sister. Both modern and fashionable, her dress was cut to hang above her ankles. It would certainly impress all concerned!

Iona prepared herself then Edwin's sisters wanted to spend time with her. When they saw the lassie dressed in her new creation, a blue velvet dress, they were aghast. "Father would never approve," was their chorus. The dress was far too short for his presence. Further it was too contemporary, glamorous, eye-catching indeed. At first they checked to see if it would be possible to lower the hemline but discounted that idea due to the time. Iona was deeply saddened and hurt by this development. She had made a concerted effort at some financial cost to present herself as a very modern miss. It was just too much. Martha lent Iona one of her dresses; they toned down the appearance in order not to inflame their father's temper.

The nurse approached the sitting room in a somewhat melancholy mood, and in some trepidation, to meet the young man's formidable relation. His reputation preceded him. Shown in by Charlotte, who had the aplomb to break the ice; the introduction made, she left. Trevelyn flicked open his pocket watch then returned it to its waistcoat pocket. The girl was awestruck by the aura emanating from the man and his surroundings. He stood in front of a granite fireplace. Behind him a truly inspiring original painting by George Stubbs, of a horse and its owner — something of an unusual possession for a man not given to materialism, when there were philosophical and spiritual concerns to wrestle with. However, he had treated himself upon the occasion of its purchase.

The meeting was more of a question and answer session between the two generations. Trevelyn made it clear that his son was destined to run Chyancelt Farm. There were opportunities for expansion along the route of the River Fal, and even north westwards towards Kea and Gloweth. If such a man is given to moments of excitement, then this was it. He believed that he had served God well and his estate could and would prosper. He was anxious for his progeny to continue farming in Cornwall, it had been that way with his family since probably before the Civil War.

They discussed the McNiven family at length; Trevelyn approved of their church-going but promoted the benefits of Methodism. He patently approved of the lassie's grit, her moral strength but it was her zest for life and the twinkle in her eye that confused him It had sadly been a very long time since passions had stirred him; the character thus before him, confused his senses. During this time alone the farmer twice chose to invoke his sincere thanks to the nurse for saving the life of his only son.

The girls knocked at the sitting room door, bringing with them their brother. He walked around Iona brushing his hand against hers, by way of giving her confidence now that he was there. With Charlotte in the room the decibels increased, and everyone relaxed. Mary Lee called the gathering into the dining room where they ate heartily: meat from their own farm via their butchers shop, Cornish cream and butter from their own dairy. There were certain tastes that were new to Iona, who gathered all available knowledge concerning the food.

The holiday passed very well. Trips to Penzance and Falmouth (by boat) — Agnes, now pregnant with her third child, dining upon chowder[4], mackerel and lobster varieties. Perranporth with its truly wonderful beach and bracing climate. To old tin mines, Truro, its market and a couple of concerts. Both Sundays were dedicated to the Lord, through his accepted channel the chapel. Walking the fields down to the Truro River then along to the River Fal. Crossing the Fal using the King Harry Ferry and over to St Mawes.

The nurse experienced a completely new lifestyle. She rose early to observe the milking and care of animals, absorbing much that hitherto was unknown to her. She left as she had arrived, by pony and trap, delivered to Truro Train Station and the care of the Great Western Company. The couple pledged an early repeat; they wished to keep one another's company again and soonest.

Edwin and Iona were evidently in love; the entire household and staff were struck by the intuitive rapport between the couple. Further, they were surprised by Iona's interest in farming. She was not in any way put off by the smells, mess and sheer hard work associated with caring for animals.

During the first evening alone together Trevelyn Senior called his son to discuss the situation. He had warmed to the idea of this girl; he could envisage her as a farmer's wife, running Chyancelt Farm. Father and son relaxed their attitude towards one another. The ongoing work of the farm took the concentration of the two men, as harvest with its associated long hours and concerns regarding weather overtook them, but the mind of the younger farmer was elsewhere.

Letters continued to be written by each of them until, after Michaelmas (Sept 29 – feast of St Michael) and following harvest festival, one from Nottinghamshire offered a Christmas holiday to the suitor from Cornwall. He replied immediately then set about explaining his intentions to his father! Edwin would travel three days before Christmas returning just after New Year. Iona had worked continually since the summer, adding to her own duties when others were sick. Matron Barber had consented to the leave.

Prior to his journey 'up country' and during the livestock market before Christmas, Edwin stole away from the throng to visit a number of shops. Nobody upon Messrs Cornish and Company's property seemed to notice; they were all too engrossed with animals prices and bidding.

Visiting Cecil Roberts the outfitter he collected a new suit and black bowler hat. His existing bowler he considered too shabby now for visiting purposes. A ladies dress shop provided him with gifts; Mrs Gill assisting with the decision making. Following trips into Criddle, and Smith & Vage, the jeweller, he returned to the pony and trap left parked in Cathedral Garage under the archway by the side of that great building, and rode home. He felt very satisfied with his expedition. Though unaccustomed to such pursuits, everyone concerned made his endeavour both easy and enjoyable. Most of those who assisted him noticed the twinkle in his eyes; he was gently teased by more than one proprietor.

Father Trevelyn would spend Christmas with Martha; chapel activity and the social round was quite intense around this time and he did not wish to stray too far. Milking and feeding was ongoing so deserting the property was difficult.

Arriving in Nottinghamshire, leaving the train platform, Edwin was met by Fraser, one of Iona's brothers. He had leave from the army and like his younger brother had been serving in France. They intently discussed the course of the war. By now everyone seemed to know someone killed or injured. There was a marked effect upon a generation already. In common with others however they had enormous difficulty discussing the subject, other than with those of their own or similar experience. Mrs McNiven provided truly magnificent fayre and Christmas passed with joyous celebration, although her other daughter Fiona seemed to provoke continual argument due to her radical thinking, especially as much of it was impractical.

Trips into Nottingham indeed Hucknall Torkard and Mansfield too, gave to the young man a new perspective on industrial Britain. The mining industry of Cornwall centred particularly around Redruth and Cambourne. It was similar to Nottinghamshire coal mining, but much harder, dirtier work. The factories containing many workers were a revelation though. People were different, less relaxed in the towns, they spoke slower than the West Country, and used certain unique words and phrases in their speech. The differences were less stark to a man who had served within the army — where all types mingle and merge with the collective nature that gears them to a common cause.

All of the Christmas presents were well received, especially a ruby brooch sold to Trevelyn by Messrs Vague & Company. It was to complement the blue velvet dress made especially for the introduction to father but denied an outing upon that occasion. Iona was choosing to wear the dress upon 'state' occasions now. Prior to New Years Eve Trevelyn spent some time alone talking with Mrs McNiven and Fraser; kitchen talk. On New Years Eve the household went to a party. For Trevelyn this was his first Hogmanay party.

Prior to midnight Trevelyn and Iona left the throng, selecting the garden for a breath of fresh air and a moment of quiet. As the count for midnight was heard from the house, around the garden the farmer asked for the hand in marriage of the nurse. She replied, "No." Edwin was confused by the reply when everything seemed to have built up towards this moment. The playful lassie then said, "If you asked me again from a position of bended knee I may just consider your proposal." The man's face relaxed, he exhaled in relief and fear, then fell to one knee as the cheer rang from the house for the New Year. Now holding her right hand whilst looking up into her eyes he asked her if she would marry him, to which she immediately blurted out, "Yes; soonest!" He rose; they held each other and kissed for a long time. As the New Year cheering increased, with people jumping up and down, yelping and whooping, the now two parties were intensely engrossed in their own worlds. It was 1917......

Two days later, saying his goodbyes to the McNiven family Trevelyn escorted his fiancé into Nottingham. They had a couple of hours left before she resumed her duties and he caught a train. Walking around the retail part of the city they looked at various jewellers before spotting the gems and setting that pleased her in a shop in Angel Road; they entered John Perry's emporium and bought a sapphire with diamond-encrusted ring, said a few words to one another and completed the ceremony with him placing the ring upon the fourth finger of her left hand. They kissed, thanked everyone for their assistance and left to journey to their separate destinations. Now they were visibly bound to one another.

CHAPTER VIII

Upon his return to the farm Trevelyn did not immediately inform his father of his new circumstances; instead he went into Truro to seek the advice of his sister Martha on how best to handle father. This was to be a delicate mission. Martha and Edwin spoke at length. They decided that the sooner father knew of his son's intentions the better.

Before resuming his routines at the farm the young man asked for private time with his father. They had eaten a meal without saying too much, as the housekeeper was nearby. After the food the two men retired to the sitting room. The younger man stared out of the window, looking down the fields, hedge by hedge to the Truro River, over it and up the other side. He was mentally tracing shapes with the fields and hedges. Finally plucking up courage to speak his piece he announced that he and Miss Iona McNiven were now engaged to be married; he talked at some length regarding the circumstances. Accepting what he now believed to be the inevitable the older man thanked his son for his straightforwardness and stated that Iona would be welcome to live with her new husband upon the farm. He realised that it needed a woman who had a vested interest in the place, actually involved in running it. He congratulated his son on finding such a beautiful young woman to marry and wished him well for bringing children into the world, his mind overriding his own sad experience in that regard. Then he talked about the farm and the cattle buying business, together with their associated enterprises. He accepted his son's vision for his future life.

"There is more," intoned the young man. "Father, I wish to leave Chyancelt Farm and Cornwall in order to buy my own farm somewhere further upcountry."

The words hit the older man as though a bullet; he stumbled back into a chair open-mouthed. "Leave Cornwall, leave my farm. This is your home, your country; it is part of us and we of it. Please God tell me that he is not serious," he murmured, holding his head in his hands. In contrast the young man was full of enthusiasm for his intended venture. He proposed to marry later that year and move into his own farm during the Michaelmas changeover. His new wife was going to become a poultry farmer: chicken, geese, ducks, turkeys. He would build dairy and beef herds, together with sheep, which would be complemented by arable land.

It was now clear to the older man that the young couple had set their intentions upon following their own path. Then the older man became angry with his son, calling him 'irresponsible'. "How will Chyancelt Farm continue when I become older? With only one son and three daughters, who will carry on the farm?" There was no answer. The spirits of the two men were completely at odds, one high, one low; differing in such a fundamental way, they rowed intensely. Every fault that one saw in the other surfaced.

A very sad episode played itself out, providing no winners. A chasm now existed between them. The younger man resumed his work upon the farm. Father and son communicated little, sometimes only through the staff. In his spare time Edwin trained and coached his horse Poacher, who was progressing.

He wrote to a number of town and city auctioneers and agents who offered farms for sale. Some estates were selling off farms; the war caused much uncertainty; confidence ebbed and flowed with the news from the Continent.

Part of the younger man's request to his father was to be allowed certain capital to be released from his estate which would enable him to borrow from a bank; sufficient to buy a farm. From the start his father had spotted this weakness in the plan as a way of delaying matters. In his mind he could delay it sufficiently to allow the marriage to occur, the couple then to return to Chyancelt Farm and once there, although looking for a farm 'up country' he might somehow thwart the idea, Especially so if young Iona fell pregnant. That alone might concentrate the mind of the younger man.

Trevelyn Senior now clamped down upon his son using the telephone stating it was for the use of the business. Not that many calls had been possible. Instead, the couple relied upon a very efficient Royal Mail postal system, or if sending a package to one another used the railway freight that was equally efficient.

During important religious festivals such as Easter, the young farmer sent his fiancé joints of meat, Cornish cream or butter. Placed upon the train in Truro by six-thirty a.m., it arrived in London during the afternoon, transferred across the city and would be available in Hucknall Torkand or one of the nearby rural stations by mid-evening. One of the McNiven family was then dispatched to collect the parcel. Their taste for Cornish-produced food was now developing!

During 1917 the couple managed a short stay at one another's homes; only a single occasion each. Their intention to buy a farm was thwarted not by father but the singular lack of suitable premises. Either too small a holding to support their intended enterprise, or too large and expensive. The condition of some was quite appalling. There had been an agricultural depression between 1874 and 1914. With the North American prairies now producing vast surpluses, Australia too, those geographically huge countries given birth to by the British Empire were benefiting from the economy of scale.

Since Robert Peel's conservative government had repealed the Corn Laws a generally non-interventionist, free trade had perhaps unintentionally led by 1900, to a decline in the countryside. There was a rising demand for more food in Britain with the fast growing population. The vast acreages of America and Australia coupled with developments in chemical fertilisers, deep drainage of land, stock breeding involving advancing some, retarding others, together with the invention of machinery, caused their cheaper imports to be drawn into Britain. Then from 1874 the good prices paid for wheat were hit by bad harvests, combined with a prolonged fall in commodity prices throughout the world. Sadly perhaps it was the European war that gave back to the British farmer his worth within the community.

With continental Europe predisposed to overrunning one another's countries and brutalising their fellow man the war begun in 1914 had produced a German U-boat submarine; together with surface vessels, a naval blockade of the British Isles. Farmers were required to produce more food. The sight of fallow acres growing thistles and large weeds called fathens, their owners unable to afford even seed to plant, gradually disappeared. The reasons which assisted the deterioration of homes and barns too were ironically reversed by the terror of war.

The development of the railways had further stimulated the distribution of agricultural produce. Hardships within both rural and urban communities were often alleviated by the growth of allotments since the 1880's. It spurned an entire culture of its own. Sometimes, if only to escape an allegedly nagging wife, or to play darts in the hut on site!

Having failed to locate a farm in readiness for the Michaelmas changeover of 1917 the couple re doubled their efforts as 1918 arrived.

There was no let-up in the practice of war around Europe and far beyond, indeed Iona had two brothers still fighting in France. However the need for home-produced food, combined with difficulties importing from across the seas, was impacting upon the value of freeholds. They did not want to pay inflated prices due to economic and political circumstance that may change.

As June passed into July a most terrible land battle commenced in the Somme. During the first morning shells were heard exploding in south east England. The loss of life was on a scale to rival even the past four years. Even the war-weary country was shocked. However it signaled the end of the conflict, for just four months later an armistice was signed. The war was over. It was described as: "A war to end all wars", further, a global wide war — dubbed a World War. Both of Iona's brothers returned. Mrs McNiven was very, very happy. The scene was now set for another very happy occasion; a now somewhat delayed wedding could take place, with both families in full attendance.

Edwin again pressured his father to release capital to a bank by way of proof of intent. His patient pleadings of the past two years had given way to frustrations on both sides. The older man desperate to invoke primogeniture, (exclusive right of inheritance to the oldest son); the younger one wanting his own enterprise and commercial freedom.

Edwin had worked as a student farmer for a period of two years upon an estate farm in Gloucestershire belonging to Lord de Vere, under the tutelage of his farm manager Major Symmonds. That was between the ages of 19 and 21;the experience led to the formulation of many ideas such as any mentally lively student should generate. Ideas evolved concerning a well rounded farming enterprise, less specialized than Chyancelt Farm. The de Vere estate did however enjoy many advantages over the average farmer it had to be conceded.

Iona visited Cornwall for Christmas 1918 and New Year 1919. The usual events at St Mary's Wesleyan Chapel took place, with the addition of concerts at Truro Cathedral. The extended family attended en masse. During the holiday the family attended polite gatherings of trades and professional people, at which the Anglican Bishop Gray had circulated. Like a pioneer, a 19th century American frontiersman or an Israeli on a Kibbutz, he was driven. A particularly social cleric he was anxious to build bridges since Truro Cathedral was relatively new. Bodmin as a religious centre had lost out and disappointment of that nature can linger. The Cathedral school was building itself an increasing reputation and he wanted to encourage the sons of local people to join the cathedral choir, which would attract higher qualified musical directors from elsewhere to look at Truro. If only they could prove themselves worthy.

During the holiday, Edwin with Iona at his side, tackled his father regarding release of capital. It was a nervous moment. The older man once again said his piece, causing a very sad and poignant interlude. Finally he capitulated. Delay and prevarication were no longer an option, the two in his presence were a couple, and would not be divided now. He would never be able to understand why any man, especially a man of the land, would seek to leave Cornwall; but there it was. This one wanted to.

Trevelyn Senior assented to the transfer of a capital sum to his son's bank account and that was that. Having secured the capital, his bank would release funding on the basis of receipt of a financial and working plan supplied to them. The couple made arrangements to view properties during Easter and before the hay cutting. Iona left Truro knowing that she was in reach of forming in effect a double partnership with the man she loved, and whose life she had been instrumental in saving; it was a defining moment for her.

During 1919 Edwin put much time and effort into selecting the right property. By late spring he had found a place with house, barns, milking parlour and 280 acres. It was about 15 miles from the small city of Thurlchester which had a good railway link west to Bristol and Bath, up to Birmingham and over to London. The fortnightly livestock market coincided with an auction on a monthly basis and the city fruit, vegetable and general market weekly on Wednesdays.

An ancient cathedral city with its assize courts, the magnificent building was begun in 1220 and finished around eight years later. An associated cathedral school and other good schools prospered due to the City Society; a charity that owed its wealth to Lord Horace Abernethy; an inventor, former industrialist and philanthropist who left land and a dowry to Thurlchester from the proceeds of his unique and patented seed drill and other agricultural innovations. His implements sold worldwide until the internal combustion engine changed forever the face and nature of agriculture.

Further the city had prospered with the manufacture of the implements and the visits from worldwide, of people involved within their own countries' agricultural sectors. Such was the tradition in the area of best practice throughout agriculture and horticulture that several members of Parliament for the city and its environs had become ministers of agriculture. Traditionally the city had selected its parliamentarians for their knowledge of the land. The production of the nation's food was taken seriously, innovation of any kind in that sphere encouraged. A thankful nation had just received a practical lesson in that subject during the

German naval blockade of Britain, and would surely remember it. He who would promote relying upon imported food would indeed be indicted as a fool now.

Having selected an affordable and seemingly ideal farm, Edwin arranged a further trip to the property for Iona. They viewed it together; she concluded that the house although sound in structure could best be described as 'having potential'. The couple agreed between themselves an affordable amount to pay for the farm. After an exchange of letters it was agreed that from Michaelmas the freehold property known as Assers Farm in the parish of Thurlmede Parva would change ownership. Having secured their home and livelihood base they arranged with Mrs McNiven and brother Fraser, a wedding date of February 16th. That being 1920 and over four and a half years since their rather inauspicious meeting. There was much to do.

*   *   *

Trevelyn, father and son, enjoyed an expedition to Jersey where they bought cattle: Guernsey and Jersey beasts for both milking and beef. Having returned with them, all were fed and nurtured for a few weeks, then some of the stock was sold off through Truro livestock market; a few more were sold to interested parties in villages along the River Fal. Men from either side of the Carrick roads, the deep and wide waterway passing Falmouth, and into the Atlantic Ocean. Men who perhaps kept a small holding in alliance with another means of earning would buy a cow, or a pig. Word of mouth spread around Devoran, Feock, St Just-in-Roseland and Mylor that animals were available from a farm with a knowledge of stock beyond comparison.

It provided a cash flow. For Trevelyn it financed the expedition, and enhanced the quality of milk and beef production in the area. The remaining stock was kept at Chyancelt Farm or reserved for subsequent movement to Assers Farm, after the marriage. Transportation was arranged for the end of February, involving certain cattle, pigs and Edwin's horse Poacher. The railway company had little difficulty arranging this in association with a lorry freight company, for the final leg. There were other deliveries arranged for that period too.

Following harvest Edwin made his formal break with Chyancelt Farm, and his father's greater enterprise. He needed to carry out much preparatory work to his own barns in readiness for milking; sties for pig rearing; to hedges and ditches that had fallen into disrepair; gates that were hanging; posts leaning due to rot — a variety of ongoing low level maintenance associated with any property. This was the time of year to prepare. Also he needed to plough a certain acreage in readiness for cropping. In order to accomplish this he spoke to locals who offered assistance in return for a wage. Some arrived with their own tools, others required everything supplying.

The house, frankly was inhospitable; lacking the woman's touch for some time, needing warm blood inside it. Iona was rather concerned about Edwin's physical health, as cold damp conditions were ideal circumstance for promoting a relapse of Rheumatic Fever. Although strictly speaking the cause was actually unknown, (there were no diagnostic laboratory tests then for the disease), it was essential that he did not replicate the conditions of Belgium and become ill again. Fires were lit in the house and kept going. There was a plentiful supply of wood, especially ash which was ideal as it did not spit and burned hot. As trees were pruned or felled if dead they were cut straight away for house fuel. Frost subsequently did not accumulate upon the inside of the windows. Its beautiful patterns no longer finding a welcome. A manure heap that had built up over several years was distributed in its entirety. The new enterprise would generate plenty of its own! Both inside and outside, the property quickly reflected signs of care in preparation for living and working, yet with no shortage of projects for the oncoming season.

CHAPTER 1X

February arrived; the couple married within St. Mary Magdalene Church, at Hucknall Torkard. A traditional Anglican wedding ceremony with an inspiring address from the officiating clergyman applicable to both the happy couple and indeed all present too. The parish church where the remains of Lord Byron and his ancestors were buried was typical of British churches where the local peoples history and conduct, especially in battle, was commemorated. National, especially constitutional and ecclesiastical history too was omnipresent.

Leaving the church to the ringing of the solitary Angelus Bell cast in 1315, Hucknall unusually, did not have a full peal of change ringing bells yet; thus the sound emanating was more as though from Southern Europe. An enthusiastic throng cheered, waved and threw confetti, rice and dried rose petals in the winter sunshine. Outside the gateway and upon the little square Mr John Tudbury & Company, a Cab Proprietor of some note, had arrived with his latest charabanc. As the staff from the library just by the church gateway, emerged from within to add their own congratulations the couple were whisked off to their wedding breakfast.

At the hotel reception for family and friends there were several single young nurses attending; perhaps expectant, hopeful even of meeting a suitable young man. These occasions do sometimes have an unusual effect upon the female of the species, especially the unattached ones.

The couple honeymooned in Scarborough for a week, during the holiday visiting Iona's Aunt Mary who had moved there recently since selling her Derbyshire hotel. She was now a far more relaxed person and offered a wealth of advice for running a small business.

The couple subsequently arrived at their farm brimming with ideas. Edwin first escorted his wife into a field where he showed to her a hen house. Perhaps 30 feet by 10 feet, with a pitched roof, sitting upon stilts; it was the wedding present that she most wanted. Despite the recipient not being required to unwrap such a large present they both excitedly examined the new structure. Hens were to be delivered soonest. The start of her part of the enterprise. She intended to breed chicks, rear them for egg laying and the table. Further, geese, ducks, turkeys and guinea fowl would follow once the hens were established. An adventurous learning cycle now followed.

Edwin had received the milking cows, and steers, some pigs too, from Cornwall, and made preparations for expansion with a bull and a boar, who could both be rented out for their unique services. Inside the house much decoration was needed. Some of the walls were up to half an inch thick with old paper which when removed revealed enormous spiders within air pockets. Complete redecoration was in fact necessary.

A few days after moving in, a consignment of freight arrived from Truro. It contained unwanted furniture given by family members trying to assist, and other new items, as presents. Father had sent a bureau-style desk for use when doing the farm accounts; a carved folded down surface with drawers underneath; the piece would complement any room. That was made by Messrs Criddle & Smith of Truro. From another company, John Julian, a gentleman's chair arrived with its complementary ladies' chair. These were for the farmer and his wife to place either side of their sitting room fire.

Before the couple could write back to thank their relatives, a long letter arrived from Martha, congratulating them upon their marriage and informing them that Agnes had given birth to her third, a boy. This offered the Provins a chance to pass on their own farm. With Charlotte having two boys, and Martha one of each, father was now the proud grandfather of seven. Iona and Edwin were overwhelmed with work and did not reply immediately. When they did it was to formally to thank everyone for their generous gifts and to announce the birth of their first child in December. A flurry of letters returned, including one from father who had found many references from the Holy Bible, by way of assistance.

1920 proved a very productive year for the newlyweds. Economic confidence was returning following the war. The influenza pandemic was over. Borrowing his father's ideas on building up the farm, Edwin added to the milking cattle and soon needed a herdsman. The seven days a week, twice daily routine provided a monthly income. The milk cheque ensured cash flow. A more long term enterprise was the herd of bullocks and steers; three years of feeding would lapse before there was a return.

The pigs were now developing and would expand in numbers as income from the eggs, chickens and milk produced sufficient capital to re-invest. Very many people in villages kept a pig, sometimes two. In addition ducks were popular. Those with a little more land might buy a cow. Either way, Edwin saw a potential for selling day-old chicks for rearing, young pigs for bringing on and a few cows too. A 'farm door' retail side would offer a range of oven ready fowl, eggs and fresh milk. Arable land for animal feed would develop as the fields were won back from weeds and lack of general care.

Before Christmas Iona gave birth to a son: Edward. She could no longer cope with everything: house, poultry, back door sales. So they employed a girl from a village towards Thurlchester who would live in during the week and run the house, assisting where necessary with the poultry. Josie, aged 18, had not particularly enjoyed her working life in a laundry where crude women discussed a lot of filth, humiliated one another, played silly practical jokes and chose a girl to ignore for a few days, creating silence around her; their behaviour was petty and the girl could not understand them. She fitted in at the farm straight away, and was able to either cycle or catch a bus to and from work.

With assistance in the farmhouse and a herdsman outside, it was subsequently decided to employ a general farm labourer. Fred Upcroft had worked at a nearby farm but was seeking more money. Having just passed his 21st birthday Fred asked his previous employer for a higher wage. The farmer had prevaricated although it was understood that a rise was due when coming of age. The employee then rather hastily rowed with his employer, which caused bad feelings to develop. The two men quickly had little regard for one another and the employee decided to seek an alternative post. Hearing that Trevelyn was gradually expanding encouraged the man to seek a future with him. Further, on the day that Fred had arrived to look around the farm he had spotted Josie. Ever a cheeky lad with something to say he teased Josie, who giggled and skipped off. When Trevelyn asked Fred about his love-life he dismissed his own girl Bethany as being of little use, 'because her knicker elastic was far too tight and needed loosening'. Trevelyn spluttered at the quick retort and realised that the young man would be something of a handful, but his energy levels and drive marked him as a potentially very good worker, and so he employed Fred.

With more staff and increasing the number of animals, the farm assumed a life of its own. There was always something happening. One afternoon a local man brought some cows over, for the bull to do his duty upon. Fred took charge, but had called Josie out of the scullery upon some pretext. She stood in the yard where the bull was corralled and cows were being shown to him. As the bull started to perform those duties that he was there for Fred began a graphic commentary, making favourable comparisons between himself and the bull. Josie shrieked and ran, passing Trevelyn en route, back to the scullery where Iona was dressing poultry. The account of the incident horrified her and caused husband and wife to discuss the matter. Independently, they spoke to both parties and told Fred to tone down his attitude towards the girl. However Josie though was secretly flattered and actually enjoyed the attention.

Iona was pregnant again. They needed to decorate another bedroom. Gradually the couple were winning in the battle to make the farmhouse a home. Their working days were long. Time off together was unknown; there were insufficient daylight hours to carry out every task that they wished to accomplish, however the staff that they had hired were pulling their weight and profits were sufficient to keep on re-investing. During the pregnancy Iona became very tired and was unable to keep a wary eye upon Josie. One day she head Edwin shouting something about 'a randy little hound'. Not having any dogs upon the farm yet she wondered what on earth was going on. Running out of the house and into the yard, across to the hay and straw barn she noticed her husband waving his arms, shouting and pointing. Entering she saw Josie, lying on the straw, her ample breasts hanging out and her skirt with layers of petticoat rolled up. Fred was huffing and puffing, fastening buttons, attempting to offer an explanation for a situation that needed no explanation at all. The pair of them were then warned about their activity. They gave the farmer and his wife a solemn undertaking to behave. Fred had not served in the military and lacked a reverence for authority. His brains were governed by his urges and unfortunately Josie found his kind of naughtiness particularly interesting.

Some weeks later with Iona shortly due to give birth, whilst eating breakfast with Josie who just sat staring at hers, the girl jumped up, ran to a sink and retched. The former nurse just sighed and said, "Young lady you are pregnant; does your mother know?" The girl burst into tears, fell upon her employer's shoulder and shook as she sobbed. Fred was called in; Trevelyn too; the four of them sat and discussed the situation. It was decided that as a matter of urgency they must both explain the dilemma to their parents, speak to the parson, who Iona would pre-warn, then marry as quickly as the law would allow. A momentum followed, whereby matters were sorted out with a speed that even Trevelyn's bull would have found hasty. Within the month the banns were read in church, and people rallied around to produce a wedding that would remain in the young couple's memory for ever. A small rented cottage was found in the village; two up and two down, but a home. Iona then gave birth to a daughter Ruth. Trevelyn remarked that what with Fred, his bull, the boar and now his wife, this was truly a fertile place to be, and mused upon the next harvest.

During little over six years of marriage Trevelyn and his wife produced five children: Edward and Ruth, Charles, Callum, and then unexpectedly, Heather.

The farm bred and nurtured a range of poultry; the large stock animals were breeding as required, and with complementary arable land producing winter feed the business was viable and the bank very happy. So too were the employed work force of cow herdsman, pig man, labourer, Fred, (who now had two children and a liking for beer), Josie, and a part-time lady who 'picked' or plucked the poultry before dressing it ready for sale and generally assisted Iona.

Attending Thurlchester stock market one day Trevelyn decided to also call into his bank and see if they would, in principle, lend further monies to him for the purchase of freehold land. He needed to buy more land adjoining his farm. Every facet of the enterprise would benefit from more land. To his surprise he was not offered an appointment but asked to wait. Presently an under manager called him to the manager's office, whereupon they congratulated the farmer upon his work and offered him a greater sum than he had in mind. The problem was that there was not sufficient land likely to be for sale adjacent to his farm matching the sum of money that the bank was willing to lend, or rather encouraging Trevelyn to borrow. It was an interesting exercise though; commercial confidence can be a very subjective area.

One problem for Trevelyn was that his herd of cattle and the pigs dictated the use of much of his land. Their need for winter food, hay, and root crops for the pigs controlled much of his rotation. If the weather was kind enough he obtained two cuts of hay from the designated grass fields. Nature could not however be relied upon to assist with a perfect harvest. Further, was the desire to introduce sheep, who may need hay, swedes, kale, rye, winter barley, vetches and rape to contribute to a balanced diet. To achieve an ideal rotation cycle he would need land, and much more of it.

Trevelyn's idea required large sums of money to be spent before any return was visible. He had been teased around Thurlchester for considering leaving farming to 'dog and stick it'; a reference to sheep farming. Truth to tell he knew that carpet manufacturers wanted the hard wearing Devon and Cornwall Longwool sheep, with high quality wool. With their lambs able to be shorn at six months old, the breed produces a good carcass of meat too, whether fed grass or fodder crops. It further made sense to his cash flow and therefore the bank.

Another breed that had caught his eye was the Shropshire, who can adapt to any climate and soil. Therefore inferior acreage which failed to yield good quality crops could be grazed by the sheep. The Shropshire being particularly resistant to ailments are robust, producing lean meat for the butcher's shop. There was a ready supply of commodity factors and wool staplers who would convey the wool produced to Stourbridge Fair and other wool trade marketplaces wanting the product.

Another reason for desiring a greater acreage was for poultry. The turkeys were in a specially made shed but the chickens, guinea fowl, geese and ducks were all free range, with insufficient fields available to situate more hens. During 1927 Trevelyn made a point of asking if neighbours and locals around Thurlchester market, even within the Market Tavern where men of a like mind drank, talked and even made preliminary deals, knew of the availability of freehold land.

One market day lunchtime whilst enjoying a pint of best cask bitter, Trevelyn was approached by a local solicitor who invited him aside. He did not wish to say much but implored the farmer to visit his chambers prior to leaving the city for Thurlmede Parva. Later that afternoon the farmer did as suggested. The wily old solicitor had a spring in his step and twinkle within his eye; ushering the younger man into the inner sanctum, he instructed his secretary to produce tea for two and some cake. It was the indication that this particular guest was very welcome. After seemingly endless preliminaries, some flattery, a statement of his own particular importance within the city, and the arrival of the Dundee cake no less, the law man actually introduced his point.

He was responsible for the sale of a farm holding; freehold possession was available for the empty property. These past 12 months the acreage had remained fallow. It extended to well over 500 acres in total. Peering over his glasses, now with crumbs of his favourite Dundee cake resting contentedly upon his chin, the man epitomised greed to the farmer. In serious tones with sometimes exaggerated and extended words he spoke glowingly of the potential of Regius Farm, Eatonville, within 2 miles of his own respected chambers . He and he alone could decide upon the eventual owner of the property. His importance in the matter needed to be fully understood. He knew everything about Trevelyn he stated. Producing his card, Henry Waddup then chose to introduce a material point not unrelated to the sale. Evidently the farm had belonged to his mother's second cousin, Leo Callis. Uncle Leo, as Waddup called him, died intestate.

"Due to a number of mistakes, ahem," he cleared his throat, "confusions," he finished, and coughed several times, causing the crumbs to drop upon the paperwork in front of him. "And oh, misunderstandings, you understand."

"Nothing to do with his respected chambers," he quickly added. He, Waddup was the sole beneficiary, and executor too.

Waddup was aware that the farmer could raise the necessary money; in confidence his old friend, Matthew Fore-Smith, the bank manager had told him so. He had seen Trevelyn's file!

"We were at school together you know, 'The Alienuns' here in Thurlchester may I say." Puffing with pride now, he said that he would like Trevelyn to have the privilege of buying his mother's second cousin's property. Then, almost in a whisper, regarding the particular circumstances, he explained certain things. The farm had fallen into decline, and for a year or so, no use at all. Further it had taken a considerable while for him, Waddup, to sort out the legal and financial mess of Callis.

"Very complicated you know; addicted to Laudanum, heavily reliant upon whisky. Callis never married, indeed had rarely left the farm. Callis was," he coughed, "ahem, lazy, not given to the daily rigours of work unlike the two men assembled." He coughed a dry cough again.

With his confidential knowledge of Trevelyn's ability to raise the money, he was further able to assist, for a small fee, yet to be determined, with recommending a buyer for the farmer's existing freehold. The farmer quietly seethed. Here were characters from a very small school with a shocking reputation for academic failure, producing spiritless cowards and utter snobs incapable of making their own way in life unless others provided for them, concocting a deal, breaching confidence and all standards of probity; but what could he do? The solicitor knew much about Trevelyn, as much as the bank manager. He decided to just listen, there was little that he could do; but the intrusive and parochial nature of these men was galling.

It transpired that Waddup wanted a very quick exchange, they would miss Michaelmas but his buyer for Assers Farm did not mind. He sought a one percent fee from the sale of Assers Farm, paid to him privately. When Trevelyn asked about the buyer for Assers Farm he was told that it had to remain private; a confidential sale would ensure its progress. The farmer was encouraged to externally view the empty property on his way home; then, if he was interested, to collect keys from Waddup's chambers in order to view the house and barns internally. The men parted, Waddup suspecting that he had caught his fish but had yet to land it.

Trevelyn was indeed hooked; it might provide what he was looking for: a holding large enough to run a truly mixed farm that could employ his sons and which ought to be immune to the twin vagaries of climate and economic circumstance. When pigs were down, sheep may be up. If wheat was unwanted eggs and poultry may sell. This had been his dream. Having a clear understanding of farming history he knew that circumstances do change; with, so to speak, all of the eggs in one basket, disaster can befall an enterprise. By carefully spreading the load, they had a chance of surviving. Civil and public servants never have to so carefully assess their chances of not starving. Salaried, the guaranteed cheque at the month end allows a certain complacency to evolve. Here was a man with a wife, five children, stock and staff, indebted to a bank, having survived a terrible war but always in danger of a recurrence of heart disease, now gambling everything in a push for his ultimate security and that of his children. The callous nature of the bank and solicitor unnerved him; they exhibited no ethics. What to do?

He discovered that the farm offered a potentially beautiful stone, with thatch and tile roofed house, with a dairy, and a scullery which was ideal for the preparation of poultry. A rick- yard with barns, cow shed, milking parlour and pig sties built in a square. More pig sties and other stock buildings were built beyond the square. The property ran alongside the Thurlchester Road which gave access to fields from gates both off the road and through fields. Ideal in bad weather. Along the other side ran Asser's Brook, a minor tributary to the River Kells. The ditches of the farm drained into the brook, all of which were destined for Thurlchester then beyond. With good drainage, proven soil quality, a farm house and barns needing little but sheer hard work, Trevelyn was attracted to the idea. He travelled home enthused.

Iona was naturally cautious, given their responsibilities but agreed to view the property. The following week the couple met with a clerk from Mr Waddup's chambers, on the property. A supercilious character, who looked down upon the couple, making a complaint about mud, damp, wind, indeed everything that nature could offer. He remained within his employer's borrowed car whilst the farmer and his wife explored.

The house had clearly not been decorated since Queen Victoria was on the throne, with newspapers stuffed into the chimneys. Leo Callis had lived, eaten and slept within the great kitchen area and scullery. Understanding the scale of the operation to return the house into a livable home was daunting. They conceived a plan, quickly placing it before Waddup. As he had a mystery buyer who strangely was unconcerned with the strict Michaelmas changeover, and due to the poor internal condition of the house, with necessary preparation of buildings as well, they needed two months to prepare the place for habitation by a young family.

To Trevelyn's amazement Waddup agreed. Trevelyn stated that Fore-Smith at the bank would have to agree, and to his astonishment Waddup stated that he had, then corrected himself to say he would, he believed. Very quickly contracts were drawn between Trevelyn and a hitherto unknown party who would buy Assers Farm, namely Agri-Culture Limited. Curious about the corporation and any connection between Waddup who was introducing the buyer for a fee, Trevelyn was not however given any information. He did feel though that Agri-Culture were paying the lowest price possible, and he was paying the maximum for Regius Farm. Tipping the balance was the fact that Fore-Smith at the bank was making the transaction very easy indeed with a larger than expected loan, backed up with cash flow money, an overdraft facility for the day-to-day running of the enterprise. The land was freehold with a clear title deed. Christendom, and the monarchical family as earlier freeholders had long since ceased as an encumbrance on the estate; that was an asset. But who was Agri-Culture Limited?

CHAPTER X

A delayed completion, two months following an exchange of contract, gave sufficient time to make arrangements for a move. The farmer and his wife left their staff running Assers Farm, hired local village people from Eatonville to assist during their exhausting eight weeks to bring the property up to an acceptable standard. There was no shortage of retired men in particular for the outside work upon the buildings and the land, or women of the village willing to work on a casual basis within the house. With the proximity of Christmas and the depths of winter needing more fuel for the fire and food for empty bellies, keen labour was in abundance.

The move itself was very tricky — a journey of 11 miles for the animals. The cows needed their breakfast time milking then transporting to their new fields, but the milking facility needed to be ready again by four o'clock. Cattle trucks were hired for the transportation. The hen houses were lifted onto lorries; the poultry were housed within an open cage arrangement and towed by the two shire horses that were retained.

Trevelyn himself hacked his own horse Poacher to his new stable. During the journey the caravan passed under a railway bridge. As they did so the ducks and geese all ducked as though about to lose their heads! Well not just yet anyway. It provided a family anecdote for occasions when the funny antics of animals in association with humans were invoked.

All living creatures arrived safely. The only problem was that the experience put the hens off laying for around two weeks, thus affecting customers and income. With Christmas so close the annual cull of turkeys was almost immediate. Ducks, geese, some chickens too. It provided an immediate income for the farm. The New Year ushered in a programme of cutting hedges and clearing ditches, of ploughing then sowing seeds. Daylight hours were now at a premium, milking in virtual darkness morning and evening, the barn not being lit too well made working practice difficult. An oil generator housed within its own building provided electricity for the house and barns but it was ready for renewing.

Sheep were introduced to the farm as intended. There was sufficient acreage now to grow kale and strip feed them, that is fencing off a strip for the animals to eat today, then moving it forward tomorrow thus preventing them gorging themselves. Milking cattle were fed thus too. Two breeds of pig were represented upon the farm. The Wessex Saddleback was a cross between the Essex and the Wessex, black with a white band over its shoulders and down to its front legs. The large White pigs were by now very popular for the intensive farming required commercially. Trevelyn sold a number of each breed to men with smallholdings and those with some spare garden space or an outbuilding.

The turkeys were Bronze, a heavy breed of the bird. Muscovy ducks, Brecon Buff Geese, and the hens were a Rhode Island Red cross with Light Sussex. Such was the make-up of the farm that now employed Fred the labourer and Josie his wife, who had rented a cottage in Eatonville. A cow man, pig man, shepherd and two or three casual staff assisting Iona with the preparation of New York dressed poultry, farm produced cooked meats, for example hazelet, hams and brawn. By the Christmas of 1928 even the farm cats had reason to relax, just a little.

The move to Regius Farm had prompted Edwin's sister Charlotte to visit in haste. Nothing could pass without her inspection. Further there were those who wanted to know what was happening and without an inspection Charlotte was rendered ignorant if asked. Well that was her logic anyway. Arriving before winter was over, she first provoked an incident with a character known as the 'Marmalade Man'. The farm had its sewerage collected by the local authority every week. A mains system would be installed during the next few months. Until then however a wagon drawn by two heavy horses called by and emptied buckets from an outhouse. Due to the structure and colouration of the substance that they collected, they were known as 'Marmalade Men'.

Charlotte was told not to use the outhouse around eight o'clock on Wednesday morning. Being above the usual mortal considerations effecting everyone else Charlotte insisted upon using the facility to suit herself. It happened to be around eight o'clock, and it was Wednesday. With her skirt hitched up, substantial underwear around her ankles and the omnipresent fox stole complete with fox's head around her neck, she cut a unique sight to the local authority collector of unwanted materials, who was informed upon his interruption that he should wait in the yard, she was still busy. He did as he was told.

Charlotte came with the news that the butcher's shop in Truro had been sold off, together with all of father's other business interests. He now only retained the responsibility of the farm. Martha had lost her daughter but Agnes soldiered on with her three. When she had access to Edwin by himself Charlotte placed considerable pressure upon her brother to return to Chyancelt Farm and Truro. None of his direct family or indeed the in-laws could understand his stubbornness in staying 'up country'. Being an independent spirit always comes at a price he reasoned, as he gave consideration to his building enterprise and gazed towards infinity.

✻   ✻   ✻

Regius Farm quickly gave up its history to he who understood British evolution in its broadest terms; or he who wanted to appreciate it. The land had formed part of a 'three field system' of farming in common, during and since Anglo Saxon times. It was an open field system surrounded by woodland. In 1215 Magna Carta within its clause 44, had affected protection to the nearby Forest of Aeternus together with other woodlands that impacted upon the farmland, despite not yet forming a private freehold.

According to Rudyard Kipling in his poem celebrating the Great Charter "the first assault upon right divine" gave protection to hunters and again in the separate 'Carta de Foresta' of Henry III in 1217 which picked up from the Forest clauses 44, 47 and 48 of the Magna Carta, "saving all existing liberties and free customs". Forest courts were held but restricted in jurisdiction however, forest law involved giving rights and privileges to those who fell within the geographical 'Hundred' and its acreage. It was, even in 1928, both sensible and cautious of a farmer and freehold owner to grant hunting of rabbits and pheasants to locals. Better to offer the opportunity, giving an option of withdrawing it, rather than provoke many poachers. Those who enjoyed the privilege would more than likely seek to protect it. Further, with a predominance of so many large families, hunger can so easily provoke insurrection.

One could still see evidence of the fields that had witnessed co-operation of farming 'in common' around Regius Farm. Grass boundaries or field marks divided the 'yard-lands' where a man shared a plot in different places around the village with others. Whether he was producing wheat, rye, barley, beans or oats, or perhaps leaving the field fallow, he was responsible to the manorial court decision, where he might be fined as a by-law breaker and even have his stock impounded. Tradition and custom were the essence.

Thomas Paine, the constitutional writer, who took part in both the French and American revolutions had described Britain as: "A country of custom and practice." Conservative practices clearly mitigated against a display of ingenuity or imagination, in favour of the common good. The antithesis of farming in common emerged between 1760 and 1792 as open fields were ended, parish by parish using local acts of Parliament. The Parliamentary Inclosure movement ushered in higher land values, rents and profits, improved husbandry, abolishing tithes. The owner or impropriator of the tithe, quite often the church, was compensated with a grant of land. Farming in severalty as individual enterprise was known, changed an ancient way of life. Certain common land for grazing was maintained. Farmers then built their houses away from the village, becoming physically separate from their neighbours.

Poaching of game thus became as much a political gesture and sport as a requirement to fill an empty stomach. A cautious farmer sensing the mood did not always reciprocate if his territory was breached. He was now particularly wise to sense the mood. So the land pertaining to Regius Farm passed out of the three-field system of Eatonville, with its manorial court, to one of a series of five major freeholdings. It survived through the era of Cardinal Wolsey, his monarch Henry VIII, and into private secular hands. It benefited from a national road nearby servicing the City of Thurlchester which gave easy access to markets of stock, horticulture and dry goods. Inns had prospered, the vicinity needed to support a new class of wayfaring traders, horse dealers, wood staplers, barley and wheat factors, cattle drovers too.

With the Crown grant of a borough charter and permission to hold weekly markets in 1164 by Henry II, who never relaxed his grip on church or state, the monarch gained much support from the locality through that grant. Nevertheless he lost some of that support only six years later with the murder of his 'troublesome priest' Thomas A' Beckett, and the ensuing papal interdict upon the country. Later, as the parliamentary era developed terms of the borough charter, and with the vibrancy of the market place locally the area then provided three members of Parliament.

With the demise of the so-called 'rotten boroughs' those numbers were reduced to one. Due to local agricultural innovation and production, the wise choice of that member as a man involved with, or fully understanding the ways of agriculture and the land, had caused a retention of authority and influence for the city of Thurlchester, which provided ministers and under secretaries of state for agriculture. No backwoodsmen were entertained. The benefit to the city and its agricultural hinterland was easy for all to see.

In earlier times of the ancient 'hundreds', those legal and administrative districts, the locality was under the jurisdiction of the Thurl Hundreds for both civil and criminal courts although Eatonville had a detached court jurisdiction subjected to the 'socn'or jurisdiction of the Church. It was a sort of private franchise between the era of Henry II in 1158, and Henry VIII in 1534, when it was taken into the quarter sessions of the assize courts held in Thurlchester. Until then the so called 'Eaton Stone' marked the place within the village where taxes and tithes were collected. The stone had been cut from granite in the shape of a large gravestone, then sunk into the subsoil. This was where justice was administered too. The villages' detachment from the city allowed the law to be subjected not only to the socn of the Church, also to the secular lords. An explicit royal grant had ordained this since 1064 and Edward the Confessor's time. His charter issued the previous year stated: "It is our duty courageously to oppose the wicked and take good men as models, by enriching the churches of God, relieving those oppressed by wicked judges, and by judging equitably the powerful and the humble."

The Confessor being the first king to have a royal seal and to appoint a chancellor would be later cannonised, with a posthumous cult developing his ongoing reputation and legacy. Here in Eatonville as in so many villages and townships, that legacy was omnipotent. The Eaton Stone served the village until a tithe barn was constructed nearby it around 1258 to serve both church and state. That barn held the actual property received in tax or tithe. Henry III needed taxes for his European adventures; such barns could house both the goods and collectors of those properties now taken into state or indeed Church hands. It further provided a home base for the men who would build St Etheldreda's Church, Eatonville. With easy access to the River Kells the stones for both the earlier tithe barn then subsequently the church were floated down by barge from quarries elsewhere.

The church had been built between 1269 and 1273, with delays upon the death of Henry III in 1272 when Edward I ascended the throne. Political uncertainty occurred when an autocratic, short-tempered man indicated his intentions for reform to royal government and the law. Once Edward Ist's intentions were understood the church building work was completed. Subsequently, artists supervised by a Royal craftsman were employed to paint frescoes, in celebration of the second accession of Edward IV in 1471, following his triumphant return from the low countries. His swift and ruthless actions in battles at Barnet and Tewkesbury reasserted his governance of the kingdom until 1483.

The frescoes began with God's call to Abraham in Genesis 12 to go to Canaan, and a new promised land for his descendants; they continued with celebration of the land and its bountiful produce, if treated properly. For example 2 Chronicles 7, Verse 14 where an offer by God to make their land prosperous again was like all of the 12 richly illustrated frescoes extolling and celebrating the natural world and people enjoying it, when respected.

By sending the quarried stone down the river using a barge many villages could be developed alongside the waterway, or by following a navigable tributary, upstream too. A village was thus born; its incorporation into the greater state, receiving and dispensing law and its involvement in the spiritual life of the country and development of itself as an economic unit all evolved quickly during the Norman and Plantagenet eras.

Interestingly, many cultural and political developments would remain barely changed until the Great Reform Act of 1832. The Reformation, Civil War, and plague or the Black Death, did bring other changes though.

Regius Farm then, built around 1509 during the succession of Tudor father to his second son had undoubtedly replaced an earlier construction of around perhaps 1270, which itself may have replaced a wooden structure constructed some time during the Wessex dynasty. Stones that were clearly parts of earlier foundations; coyne stones — those large dressed corner stones — would appear in the garden, orchard and yard areas from time to time. The village had also developed a large allotment facility, rented from the Church, some 54 holdings were in crop. Certain men rented a double holding. It was typical of the generation who had served in the 1914-1918 war that they turned away from politics and every facet of life concerning the state and its governance, to the land. The gentler world of sabotaging their neighbour's prize marrow before the village show held a greater allure for them evidently.

A primary school built in 1875 using the classic Victorian architectural design of high windows allowing the passage of much light but no vision of the earth, in order not to distract those who were there to learn, was situated near to the church. Indeed it was a church school, and every second Friday the incumbent vicar took morning assembly. The vicar lived in 'The Parsonage' an early 18th century pile of stone within its own grounds, and like the churchyard, festooned with yew trees; a dominant cedar tree whose forebears hailed from Lebanon graced the front. Annual village fetes were held there together with other appropriate social functions.

A mill stood at the junction of Assers Brook and the River Kells. It was a water mill driven by the combined power created by a confluence of flowing water. Previously hosting many generations of those passing skilled tradesmen of the Tramping Society of Fraternal Journeymen Printers. Beyond it a mill pond little more than two feet deep; a wide crossing place for cattle and men. There was a butcher's shop, post office and general stores, bakery, blacksmith, saddlery, carpentry and joinery business and a thatcher.

Together with the Eaton Alms public house, all employed local people, being village centres of economic activity; places to exchange money for goods and gossip. There were farm gate sales of eggs, poultry, milk and cooked meats at no less than three of the farms. Trevelyn and his wife would quickly offer a complete range of meat and produce.

A small engineering workshop which had retailed and repaired bicycles was emerging as a garage, servicing motor cars, lorries and motorcycles. There was about the place a self sufficiency, despite the proximity of the city. The baker would rent a market stall in Thurlchester during the week prior to the major festivals of Easter, Whitsuntide, Harvest Festival and Christmas; his range of bread and cakes differing sufficiently from those in the city to warrant proffering his wares. A change was as good as a rest for his occasional customers. The village had an ongoing vibrancy to it other than on Wednesdays when Thurlchester market was supplied by a bus route. A generation now leaving school, tended to journey into the city for work though. Some used a bicycle, others a bus; there had been a change particularly since the war. Agricultural staff were still readily available, however.

Despite the vagaries of climate and economic circumstance men were by instinct inclined to the land; fresh air, honest work, the natural rhythms of nature were almost irresistible. Morning and evening saw men crisscrossing the village making for their employer's property clutching a lunch box, sometimes referred to as a 'docky box', the quality of its contents depending upon their wives' culinary talents, or what was affordable. The former village squire's home, a Jacobean structure, attracted the largest number of farm staff; twenty-seven in total, as the small estate was a self-contained unit.

Whilst the man who would have previously been called squire was a serving army major, his farm manager and the gamekeeper who both lived within the bounds of the estate effectively ran it on a day-to-day basis. The squire's grandfather had built a village school before the state provided for education or required such attendance by statute. His ancestors were the usual interesting mixture of hard-working accumulative types; the odd eccentric, mavericks with occasionally squanderous characters, but always loyal to King and Queen and country, especially during war. Further, his support for the church set an example. Being the parish benefactor brought other responsibilities to the fore as well.

One such duty was to interview and choose a rector, vicar, or parson as and when the incumbent died or moved away. The parson commanded enormous respect even where households were non-conformist or even agnostic. Girls were expected to curtsey to his wife. He would chair the Parochial Church Council and the Secular Parish Council, whilst the squire or his representative sat in and made contributions where necessary. Traditionally the vicar had been a classicist; Latin and Greek gave these men such depth and breadth. Sometimes their degree in divinity was almost a complimentary subject; for others literally a calling from God to change direction. Earlier study which if pursued would have led to a lucrative professional career was eschewed, as duty called. War or similar catastrophic events may even have diverted his mind from secular and temporal considerations of money-making into spiritual, inspirational and benevolent working practices. A calling thus from the almighty determined that so many such characters were destined to plough a lonely furrow though, throughout their working lives. Finding the right wife to cope with a village rectory or parsonage and reduced economic circumstance was sometimes quite tricky, unless she had family experience of such matters. Sometimes highly qualified village vicars indulged in other work aside from ecclesiastical concerns: translations of ancient texts, original writing, research, even scientific experimentation, alongside a quiet devotion to duty.

Of similar stature within any village would be the doctor, that is if one did reside within the parish. He too would be drawn to his profession by way of a calling, the word 'duty' would equally apply to the true country doctor, whose labours were never from nine until five, who needed to be self-reliant and quick thinking as he worked often alone. House visits, travelling miles sometimes for the same guinea that a town or city practitioner can earn from the annexe to his own home. The practicality of so many of his diagnoses could perhaps be summed up by the boy who was taken by his mother to the village doctor with terrible stomach and intestinal pains whereupon the medic pronounced from an old saying: "You have got to eat a peck of dirt before you die." The apparent unsympathetic comment did not belie that well known fact that odd pieces of grit and dirt contained within vegetables or fruit may cause an infection, though these minor problems actually benefit the child and subsequent adult as they cause antibodies to develop which may well fight off a potentially more serious illness, or provide protection when ill. Such is the benefit of natural fresh, unadulterated food. It was the doctor's skill in diplomacy, his so-called 'bedside manner' which educated a layman, understanding that his temporary plight might be seen as a stepping stone to a later healthier life!

Categories of village people descended in a social pecking order; landed, moneyed and professional classes, down to artisans in their shops and workshops, and at the bottom rung the domestic servants and labourers. In between, authority was accorded to gamekeepers, like the wary respect that is granted to policemen or to the landlord of the local public house, who could say who and who could not drink and socialise within his establishment. Farmers, as the main producers of food and a major employer gained immediate respect if they treated their neighbours decently. Indeed approaches for employment to a man with a sound reputation was quite usual.

Trevelyn was now running a burgeoning enterprise and needed more labour. A man by the name of Copping offered his services. He did not wish for a full week, having a small holding of his own; they agreed on four days. Offering to look after the feed barn in particular and tend the pigs, he became quite protective towards his domain.

Working upon their accounts three months later, Trevelyn and his wife noticed how they had recently bought considerably more grain than usual for their poultry, meal for pigs, and other animal feed concentrates. They discussed the issue and decided to watch events. One winters afternoon, with a sharp frost closing in Trevelyn and Copping passed a cheery good night to one another. The new employee rode his bicycle off home for his meal but navigating around the corner he somehow lost his balance and fell off the machine. Thankfully the man was unhurt and a couple of people kindly came to his aid. As the rider and bicycle parted company the man lost all control of his transport which hit the road with a jolt. Attached to the back and front of the bicycle sitting over the mudguards were wooden pannier type boxes which upon hitting the ground burst open, spilling animal feed all over the road. Copping was embarrassed by the incident; the two witnesses surprised, wanting to assist, tried to gather up the man's property. Copping then became somewhat hostile. The incident might have passed unnoticed, but for one of the witnesses queuing within the baker's alongside Iona just a few days later. The woman asked after Copping and was saddened by his loss of feed for his stock. Iona agreed, became thoughtful and decided to mention the incident to her husband.

They discussed matters at length and the horror of what was about to unfold with the effect of a scandal within the village. It was not an enjoyable experience to suspect an employee of theft. The following day they both had an eye upon Copping. He carried out his work in the usual way and left on time. As he rode off the farm premises Trevelyn stepped in front of his bicycle thus preventing any further movement. An altercation developed as the employer demanded to open the wooden panniers. The men pushed and shoved each other, Copping attempting to move forward. Trevelyn, now with a leg either side of the front wheel of the bicycle and his right hand upon the handle bars, was forcing up the lid of the front pannier with his left hand. Then the men lost their balance; over went the bicycle and the men began loudly cussing, then swearing about one another. As they landed, both looked around themselves for different reasons. Copping observed his booty spewing all over the roadway. Trevelyn called out, "That's my animal feed!" The men wrestled a while until arriving with a broom Iona began smacking Copping with it. Trevelyn then told Copping that he required him off the property forever, and not to return for any reason. As the men parted company a flock of sparrows descended for a late tea and probably laughed about their own luck that evening.

News of the incidents involving Copping was eventually picked up by the regulars of the Eaton Alms, who passed it on. His working day movements had changed, which caused polite questions of him, much to his embarrassment. Gradually the hapless character found that he was shunned. The sadness of the affair was the effect upon Mrs Copping, who subsequently chose to shop weekly in Thurlchester and avoid all contact with village people. There were only losers, no winners, and much sadness following that theft.

Iona re-established her poultry sales quickly. The hens suffered anticipated nerves due to the move and ceased laying. Gradually they all began to relax and lay again. They also had to acclimatize to their new surroundings. The move caused a loss of her existing customers, however the quality of her product of free range eggs, and chickens, oven-ready, New York dressed, were sufficient to sell themselves and gain new customers from Eatonville. A few duck eggs and goose eggs sold to the village but the stronger taste was not to everyone's liking. Some women however liked to cook using the stronger eggs, whether in Yorkshire puddings or cakes, their palate actually preferred the taste. Around Christmas time geese and ducks were demanded by customers who preferred the richer meat. The Roman White geese were probably the best choice of breed. Economical, fast growing, ideal for egg and meat production. Famous in history for saving Rome from an attack by Gauls around 5 BC, they make an ideal guard for anyone's property. By sleeping with only one half of their brains and one eye at a time, they are an alert bird. Further, sales of hatched chicks to other villagers who would also perhaps keep ducks, a few chickens and a pig, was always a possibility.

Turkeys were only bred for the table, no particular local market existed for their eggs. Iona hatched her turkey eggs during late May and June. Her earliest kill would be at twenty-two weeks, depending upon the development of fat under the skin and the feathers having first moulted. The children particularly enjoyed the Turkey poults; or youngsters who at only a day-old accept human company, are cuddly and enjoy playing games; sparring is natural to them.

Within a few weeks of arriving at Eatonville Trevelyn had been spotted hacking Poacher his horse around his own land and along bridleways. It truly was his pleasure. One afternoon a red-faced corpulent man arrived during milking and requested the farmer's company. An inconvenient time for the farm; the visitor showed no interest in other peoples problems. He was not a countryman, but tried to emulate the country way of life in his appearance, use of the language and demeanour. In fact he had been a salesman, representing a clothing company. His arrogance at expecting an immediate audience despite other men's commitments reflected his working life's assumption that everyone was ready to drop their work just to give the man a hearing. Not that he had anything relevant to say.

The moment that he chose was highly disruptive; failing or declining to be discreet and go. He wanted the Thurl Hundreds Hunt to have access over Trevelyn's land. The farmer explained that it was simply not possible due to the range of stock everywhere, together with planted crops, which made it an unwelcome request. He was not philosophically against hunting, wished the man well, but needed to safeguard his livelihood. Whereupon the former salesman took against the farmer, balked and strutted about, complaining about the inconvenience. Trevelyn gave the man his answer and stated that he had better leave and take his temper with him. He was typical of a certain urban class who had made fast money but remained uncouth.

Trevelyn looked around at his staff and said, "You can take the monkeys out of the trees but you cannot take the trees out of the monkeys." Everyone laughed; it lightened the mood.

An ongoing threat was foxes, having access unhindered, and certainly a menace to poultry and young lambs, being prepared to slaughter without even an appetite. Other pests met with the severest of sanctions too, including pigeons, those wily devourers of grain. Sparrows and rooks were either shot, or in the case of larger birds a catapult would be used upon them. Men from the village would be given access, encouraged even, to dispose of them. All offered, in sufficient numbers, a meal. As families were often large, despite the Influenza Pandemic of 1919, many were grateful for legal access to the land. Treveyln preferred to make his offer openly, perhaps during a Saturday evening visit to the Eaton Alms Public House. It reduced the possibility of poaching, as those men invited onto the property would in effect police the acreage themselves, hardly wanting others to steal the offered food and sport.

When Trevelyn and his family shot a rabbit, they often gave it away to a widow or woman with a large family. This was not only the charitable approach but it built good neighbourly relations. There was a small and sometimes vociferous minority who would bad-mouth farmers; a rabbit here and there assisted with nullifying that refrain and filling a belly.

Despite everything though people of all stations in life were kind and courteous to one another. For a farmer this impacted for example as they entered his land to go blackberrying or collecting mushrooms, shutting the gates, thus protecting all stock and by not allowing their dogs to roam and frighten other animals.

It was very difficult for the farmer to get away from his own land but whenever possible Trevelyn took an opportunity to visit Cornwall; upon this particular occasion, taking the train through to Penzance, he was met by his brother-in- law George and three children. Using a pony and trap to convey their guest homewards it was driven by George's son, already a considerable horseman. The family were anxious to discuss any ideas for new crops to thus enhance their income. The excellent railway link from Penzance to London gave to them an opportunity for transporting a product quickly to market. Flowers had been mentioned and they were looking at Anemones. The fine terracotta coloured rich soil would suit the plant. They would employ part-time staff to assist cutting, boxing, packing, then transporting the cut flowers six miles into Penzance for the Great Western Railway Company to convey them to London. Clearly there would be changes at the farm.

Trevelyn stayed one night with Agnes and George then took the train to Truro, staying with Martha and the family. There he came under enormous pressure to return to the family farm. Father was clearly ageing; he had stopped riding now and suffered with arthritis in his legs. Edwin was going to face the full onslaught from his father, who could throw the Old Testament, New Testament and Apocrypha at him and still retain further philosophical argument in order to persuade his only son to return. Cornwall was an idea that lit the world, with its myths of many layers and tales of identity handed down by the bards. He vividly lived the myth to the extent that it became true. It was a deep frustration to the ageing man that his only son did not work upon his farm, yet he had simply witnessed Celtic spirit of independence in action.

Inevitably, it proved to be difficult between father and son. Polite and tense at Martha's, when Edwin visited the farm his father gave full vent to his feelings. He made it clear that he found it quite unacceptable that his only son had left hallowed turf.

Claiming that God himself disapproved he rather exceeded his logic due to personal anger. The atmosphere was lightened when Charlotte arrived in her new Humber motor car. Becoming ever more eccentric, effectively living by herself, with her husband in Burma working his rubber plantation, she farming and with a hotel in Lamorna and her boys at boarding school in Somerset. The terrifying woman steamed around as though a battleship in a storm. Charlotte announced that she had arrived to "sort things out." It was agreed that the girls and father would visit Regius Farm separately and assess what they referred to as "the prevailing situation."

That was how matters were left. Edwin returned home thoughtfully to his own Celtic wife and five children, determined to replicate his own success, and further building his estate in preparation for when his own sons were ready to assume control. Nature would surely grant this request as his attitude to and harmony with, and respect for her rhythms, reflected Virgil's ancient world, expressed within his writings 'Georgics'.

> *Who care for the land, who nourish new fruits of the*
> *earth we sow not.*
> *And send to our sown fields the plentiful rain from*
> *heaven.*
> *You too, whatever place in the courts of the immortals*
> *Is soon to hold you – whether an overseer of cities.*
> *And warden of earth you will be, Caesar, so that the*
> *great world.*
> *Honour you as a promoter of harvest and puissant lord…*

Agriculture and cultivation of the planet had followed the patterns explained by Virgil, in sympathy with a delicate balance that is the natural world. Trevelyn was in tune with nature. Big business was now frowning upon what was known and understood to be right and proper. It wanted ponds filled in, hedges grubbed, or torn down, ditches covered, invisible pipes to secretly move precious rainfall onwards and away unseen. It saw beauty alone at the bottom line of a balance sheet; not in the autumn cobwebs, or frost on a window, ice patterns over puddles, hares boxing in March or the kestrel swooping before dusk. The corporate dining room held far more allure for too many, its deep pile carpets were trod by those who despised mud and those who knew and worked in it. Trevelyn despised them, too. He returned to do what he knew was right by the land, proven for thousands of years as pastoral. Whilst Charlotte's visit did not reflect anything of a pastoral nature, she again failed to draw her brother back to Cornish soil. His new roots were evidently deepening.

CHAPTER XI

Eatonville and Regius Farm were remote from the bustle of New York City but not in any way immune from its economic activity. The collapse of the stock market with ruined men jumping to their deaths out of office windows seemed a long way from seven o'clock milking and removal of the milk churns to the farm gate for collection by the dairy. However, it was not so far away. The catastrophic effects of the Wall Street crash were to reverberate across the Atlantic Ocean and as far as Thurlchester. Money supply became tight; people stopped buying at the farm gate. Men laid off from work, killed their pigs and eked out their meals using the beast. The allotments thrived. Trevelyn was faced with laying off first one man then another, selling his stock until eventually he and Iona were left with a few pigs, milking cows and the poultry.

Almost overnight a thriving enterprise was devastated. By the spring of 1931 it was evident that vast areas of the county would not be cultivated. Where previously crops had stood, fathens, groundsel, indeed all manner of weeds and grasses would take hold. Stories abounded in Northumberland of farmers abandoning the land. Huntingdonshire was only 30 percent planted with crops. Terrible stories of hard, fully grown men crying as their animals were led away to slaughter.

Bankruptcy was rife. Thurlchester market was as though a mortuary. It was no longer pleasant being there, with such negativity. Everyone seemed to have something to sell, but there were no buyers. With five children to feed, school fees to pay, Trevelyn and his wife could not see their way clear to survive. There was much to do refurbishing the farm house which might never be carried out now. The letters from Cornwall indicated the same. Agnes and family were dependent upon milk sales, Charlotte too, and the hotel bookings were considerably lower for the summer season. Martha was cushioned from the events; with no dependency upon a bank their various enterprises continued to prosper.

Edward Trevelyn was self sufficient having long ago ceased to borrow money, combined with his strict almost puritan lifestyle, plain living with high thinking, the slump left him financially unaffected. It was his son who was suffering, having a bank mortgage to pay, a wife, five children and a commercial enterprise that needed six men full time, together with assistance in the house in order to release Iona to run her poultry business. All of the remaining men had to go now. Edwin was milking a reduced herd of cows which guaranteed a small monthly cheque and retained twenty or so pigs. His arable land and planted feed crops were ongoing. It was essential that kale and winter feed were grown to support the livestock though.

The remaining employee was Josie Upcroft, whose husband Fred was developing tendencies for too much liquor. Their reduced circumstances were relieved by the farm because Trevelyn could ensure that Josie returned home with a rabbit for the pot twice a week; eggs and a chicken could be sold to her at cost price. Fred was encouraged to plant their entire large cottage garden with vegetables, together with taking an allotment. The Church of England who owned the allotment land had reduced its rent, and with a sympathetic Parochial Church Council only collecting the peppercorn or minimal rent during the second half of the year, it offered the opportunity for harvesting with even a few sales and exchange of certain produce to occur before the rent arose. This practical Christianity was literally a godsend for some.

Josie Upcroft worked very hard keeping the farm house in order, assisting with the children, cooking, together with plucking or picking the poultry when several were killed. She was an all-round assistant. The farm gate sales of butter and Cornish-style clotted cream had dried up. There was insufficient disposable income now available. Bread and dripping would suffice.

When Martha arrived during the summer, to again persuade the family to return to Cornwall, she instead looked at her brother's problems. Having listened to him and his wife she realised that all of the necessary cuts had been made to ensure that the farm survived.

Other than selling land which ultimately would be self-defeating the couple simply had nothing else to cut, other than the throat of another pig. Martha agreed to underwrite the school fees of the older children now travelling into Thurlchester, in conjunction with father who would visit soon.

Agnes was unable to leave their farm due to the ongoing work, but Charlotte visited. Full of ideas that were less than practical, nevertheless her two sons on holiday from their boarding school made interesting playmates for Edward, Charles and Callum. Swimming competitions in the brook and river; camps with tents and fires around the spinney; riding the backs of pigs, who would squeal and run. One hilarious trick was to tie a piece of meat onto the end of a length of string, offer it to a goose, who inevitably swallowed it. Then, having let the item disappear, pull the string back thus, retrieving the meat, to the surprise of the goose! Catapults were made, bows and arrows too. A magnifying glass was used during sunny days to start a fire or held over the skin of one of the girls to create a burning spot and squeal! Ponds gave endless fun, someone always returned to the farm covered in mud or slime with stories about frogs, toads and giant dragonflies. 'Micky' the collie dog kept for sheep farming would join in; some of the cats might be unable to quell their natural curiosity and wander over. They were always looking for a friendly contact who would allow them into that forbidden territory, the farmhouse.

The church fete with its flower and vegetable show was particularly well patronised now; with ever more households self-sufficient in vegetables, allotments were at a premium with a waiting list too. The standards of entry into the village show had risen. A competitive spirit existed where it may have not always surfaced before in quite the same way. Later, during the evening, following the show the Eaton Alms conducted a roaring trade. The question: 'How large was Bert's marrow?' Well, certainly larger by ten thirty than at eight o'clock! The beer did indeed talk.

Trevelyn could now sell more piglets than in earlier years. A copper cauldron was for sale which, when situated over dry sticks which were lit, would boil up pig food. The food consisted of a mash and swill – an amalgam of all unwanted greens. Outer cabbage leaves, brussel tops, potato, beetroot, carrot and parsnip peelings. Apples and other fruit that were rotting or in some way unfit for human consumption were also thrown in. The mix would be thoroughly boiled, producing a distinctive pungent aroma, revolting the novice nasal cavity but evidently delicious for the pig who proceeded to fatten itself, almost on cue, before the inevitable. The windfall fruit may be offered as a dessert to the animal; even people who did not keep a pig would give their boy an errand to daily take the unwanted vegetables to the nearest cauldron. Nothing was wasted. Those who could afford to bought Tottenham Pudding: a dried cake version of pig swill, and fed it to their animal. It was essential that the pig did not escape from his den or pen area, as with his remarkably tough snout he would rootle up quite literally everything. A four- legged plough that would consume all in his wake, with only a nasty smell left as his trail, and a grunt of satisfaction.

The Trevelyn children began their school life at the village primary school under the tutelage of Miss Hortence Mott, before leaving at around eight years old for the city. A dear kind woman she was simultaneously a strict disciplinarian. Miss Mott had lost her fiancé on the Somme in 1918 and believed that it was her duty to retain his memory and not marry another suitor. She actually put off any potentially interested parties with a severity that hindered further conversation. Under Miss Mott was a lady now close to retiring age, working part time only; Mrs Green already a grandmother, she worked mornings only, allowing Miss Mott to split the class. Then a young lady from Thurlchester, Miss Lottie Quintin was posted to Eatonville as a student pupil teacher. Aged 17, she awaited a placement at college a year hence; biology was her main interest. She brought many school trips onto Regius Farm to assist her tuition. Country dancing was her abiding hobby; she prepared the children for a show at the village fete.

As the new term started there was an incident in the village that brought home to the children the fragility of life. A former pupil, Desmond Valentine, known locally as 'dismal' Desmond because of his moods, now aged 19, was working at Church Farm as a general labourer. Piling up straw on a stack he slipped. The straw was shiny, assisting his propulsion; with a pitchfork in his hand he somersaulted over the stack landing on the back of his neck, the pitchfork arriving a split second later in his chest. Valentine had died upon impact as his neck was broken. The inquest determined 'accidental death'. A desperately sad affair. The funeral took place at eleven o'clock one morning and the school children were prevented from going outside to play, then again at lunchtime out of respect. By the short afternoon break they were ready to let off steam, but some just cried with their faces turned away from their friends. Playtime which offered an opportunity of marbles, conkers, dice, hoops, skipping hopscotch or swapping postage stamps had no allure that day.

Miss Mott had a wide range of economic circumstances to cope with. In the now difficult times there were those children who arrived at school hungry. Some even without proper shoes. No matter who they were or whatever their background they learned to read and write quickly, their diction was corrected, manners honed; all were made fit and ready for the world of work. Fearing God, honouring the King were central to the morning service. Prayers were spontaneous. They emerged patriotic, grateful for their lot and aware of fellow human beings' needs. The Bible and its central message of love was taught with clarity. Few of her charges would ever afford to visit the Holy Land but the images stored within their minds gave to them a clear picture of the area.

The sheer decency of everything that emanated from Miss Mott's range of knowledge would fit the child well for life as it was. No child emerged illiterate or innumerate. Their handwriting was of almost copperplate standard. Quite simply there was no crime emanating from these children either.

Despite hunger and deprivation the church stayed unlocked from dawn till dusk all year around, the charity box intact and respect for charity monies intuitive. All knew that they were born free and a proper understanding of their country's history taught them why. From the Greek, history means the weight of the past bearing down upon us in the present. Only by understanding it can we assist predicting the future.

At Christmas, Miss Mott gave each child a small present. For those who were inclined, after their schooling years learning might continue within the Parish Reading Room, a single storey one-room stone construction situated on the periphery of consecrated land that formed part of the churchyard. Within the room were books, some bequeathed; others were old library books saved from being pulped. The subject matter arbitrary.

Occupying the centre of the room was a large table, an earlier alter table too decorative for the Commonwealth period of government when it was removed from the church. Oliver Cromwell's men simultaneously breaking the medieval stained glass windows, and removing statues. The former alter table now had various old tomes, very large books permanently situated upon it. Other than for private study the room could be used by the Mothers' Union, Women's Institute, Bible study groups and the nonconformist grouping who had less need for ceremony, robes, incense or bells, yet no less sincere or committed.

As economic circumstances deteriorated unemployment became rife. Village businesses let go of their staff. The village thatcher no longer had advance bookings, only the odd patching up job if he was lucky; mostly householders placed galvanized corrugated tin over the thatch. It tended to attract lightning, was noisy in the rain, but sufficed. Building jobs were non-existent. Even the publican bought more day-old chicks, geese and piglets than was usual. He built an impressive small holding and delivered eggs with bottles of beer and stout if requested. His under-the-counter horse race betting sideline virtually ceased. Quite illegal, but he had previously during better times accepted bets upon the likely winner of the Football Association Cup Final, and Test Match Cricket results. All of which would have horrified Edward Trevelyn who, arriving in Thurlchester by train disapproved of gambling, was strictly teetotal and daily sought the Lord and invoked others to do the same.

He had listened avidly to his daughter's report but wished to assess the situation himself. A strict disciplinarian, he rigidly kept time and expected others to do likewise. Arriving wearing long leather boots he first required his daughter-in-law to remove them. Sitting in the kitchen, she was employed to pull them from his legs, a quite difficult task. Then as one o'clock approached he stood by the grandfather clock, removed his pocket watch, flicked it open and enquired: "Will lunch be served at one today Iona?" The young woman bit her tongue; Josie Upcroft blanched. It proved to be a very difficult few days especially Saturday evening when young Trevelyn slipped out of the house for two hours. His restless father wanting to know about his son's whereabouts with increasing regularity, especially after the children had gone to bed, was fobbed off with his son's requirements to post letters, and see Ken Polgreen about more day-old chicks and another piglet. Whilst pacifying Trevelyn to an extent he was not told however that Ken Polgreen kept the Eaton Alms. It was hoped that he would not see the written notice over the front door — a legal requirement by Her Majesty's Customs and Excise announcing who was licensed to trade therein — when he passed the building.

The children were rendered mute upon numerous occasions whilst their grandfather spoke about many issues. He did so with sonorous tones quite often. Trevelyn Senior really delighted in his grandchildren, although they were really too young to fully understand him. His affections were deep, emotions sometimes raw. Sadly, it is rare that a younger generation fully appreciates the deeper feelings and sentiments of someone two generations older than themselves. Casual dismissal is all too easy. In time it is not unusual to reflect why grandfather or grandmother did or said this or that. War, hunger, job loss, bankruptcy, illness, drunkenness and stupidity all take their toll, building a character, honing the personality. By imbuing a child with discipline and their country's philosophy they are fitted out for most that life may choose to present, also enabling them to assist their fellow man. Human beings do have an infinite capacity for self destruction unfortunately.

Grandfather had witnessed others disintegrate. He knew how to prevent such catastrophe. His world had been one of sobriety, hard work helping others, of living with and by the land, and Holy Bible. Only later experience of the world would make the children able to appreciate his depths. The man was not an itinerant preacher in the mould of John Bunyan or the Wesley family, his speech was perhaps allegorical, born out of a personal frustration with drunkenness, stupidity and ignorance all around him. Why was it necessary for John Wesley to preach so many times to the tin miners of Redruth? During thirty-two visits to Cornwall the Wesleys lit a fire.

Trevelyn only saw the embers and wished to ignite the flames with the 'Good News'. Despite witnessing poverty he was appalled at the parallel ignorance and idolatry. Part of his life was a mission. As he left his son and family to their labours Trevelyn pledged that he, assisted by Martha, would ensure that all of the younger children were schooled in the city, their fees underwritten, giving to the next generation an opportunity after the omnipresent depression. Thus was the pattern of life on the farm now, an almost hand-to-mouth existence. Paying the bank was the all important monthly requirement; from that the family's very existence depended. With prices low, outgoings not falling in proportion, the family's options were limited. The children felt embarrassment accepting clothes handed down from their siblings. By now all were cycling to Thurlchester, then dividing up, boys and girls to their separate schools. The younger ones were sometimes jeered at for their apparent economic plight.

Farming did not get any easier with cheap imported grain from America, Australia, and other Commonwealth countries again flooding the country. Thurlchester market was depressed; business generally bumping along the bottom; cash flow was very difficult; then to cap it all fanatical European politicians were ranting again. Their ongoing interest in running roughshod over their neighbouring countries, trampling upon human rights, culling their fellow man in the name of their latest trendy ideology seemed to have no equal in the world. Old Europe was, indeed still was, a very dangerous place for a free-thinking liberal democracy to be neighbours with. Britain only knew an independent press, politicians, judiciary, proper law made by a parliament elected with national suffrage, together with judge-made law and common law. Statutory Instruments with Orders in Council making law upon the hoof is the dictator's way. Governing a country using terror was nothing new to these people; the barrel of a gun produced a surly yet resentful obedience. If the fanatics of Europe held sway Trevelyn foresaw another naval blockade, thus creating a demand for his product. It was a terrible thought.

*   *   *

Due to the necessity for the farmer to work very long hours his resistance to illness because of tiredness was reduced. He had virtually no help now. The farm required working out in all weather, getting wet, yet struggling on. A sustained and prolonged period of rain and damp over several weeks had left Trevelyn with a cold. It was very easy to develop a cold when perspiring, due to heavy work. When we relax, or ease off for a while, the body cools with perspiration upon it, a cold then quickly develops. Trevelyn needed to work on, milking twice daily with no assistance. Rapidly his condition worsened. Confined to bed the doctor was called, who looked at his notes, thought long and hard before telling Iona that it was a reoccurrence of his Rheumatic Fever. Now he was in trouble. With cows to milk, pigs needing tending, the boys Edward, Charles and Callum at school and not yet able or ready to assume a pivotal role. Iona had to buy in assistance.

She did so by finding a man with a family, out of work but honest and willing, who accepted some money and payment with foodstuffs. Eggs, milk, a ham, chicken, shooting rights for a rabbit, anything to keep food on their two tables and Regius farm in existence, hopefully pending better times.

Trevelyn quickly needed full time nursing. He sweated the bed wet, lost liquid and weight, requiring bed care to the extent that the doctor offered a hospital placement. Iona declined the offer. Her sister Fiona was a health visitor now and a very experienced nurse and due annual leave. It was agreed she would spend ten days upon the farm. The general practitioner then began visiting daily, but one day he attended twice. During the second visit he requested time alone with Iona and stated candidly his fear that Edwin would die. He warned death was likely to be the outcome. The man was exhausted, weak, suffering weight loss and his heart clearly weakened from the wartime experience. They discussed the options for the woman with five minors to feed, a farm which had obligations to its bankers, and a dying husband.

Iona was now prepared for the worse. Quite where they would go she did not know. Chyancelt Farm loomed large now...

The telegram man was unable to discern a response from the farmhouse door. Wandering around into the animal yard he saw two women and a man talking.

"Telegram for Mr Edwin Trevelyn," he said. Iona explained the situation and accepted the item which read: "Father Dead. Funeral Wednesday. Letter Posted. Martha." It had been necessary to remove the telephone as circumstances worsened, to save a few more pounds. The telegram was completely unexpected, despite the man's great age he was fit. They decided not to attempt to tell Edwin who was feverish and might , according to the doctor, "die within the hour." It would be impossible for anyone to attend. A dying man, five children, farm to keep going, the sadness and impossibility of their situation was all too clear. The next day brought the promised letter with all details. The funeral was at St Mary's Wesleyan Chapel, Truro, father's place of worship; he would be buried however in Kenwyn Parish Churchyard in Truro afterwards. Iona rushed to produce an acceptable letter for the occasion; she did however have her own problems overwhelming her.

The doctor spoke to the two sisters explaining that he felt Edwin was losing his battle. His last chance opportunity was a new option, known as sulphur drugs. He sought Iona's permission to administer this, his only and last choice of medication. The sisters readily agreed. Now grasping at straws they had to accept the offer.

Iona shared a lift with the doctor into Thurlchester; she was visiting the bank, grain merchant, the stock market and a butcher. Essentially making preparation for a sale; the option of liquidation of their assets and removal of the accrued capital pending a move was now a possibility. She literally did not know if Edwin would be alive when she returned to the farm.

The bank manager Mr Fore-Smith was delighted to see the lady, gave flourishes of theatricality in his demonstration of grief for the woman's situation. He further stated that she need not worry about a thing, he knew of buyers just waiting for the right property and that Trevelyn had proven the potential of his holding. Mrs Trevelyn was to return to the bank if events took a sad turn; he, the manager would personally handle the matter. It was an oily, gushing performance. Iona did not enjoy the experience. The man was like a character from a Charles Dickens' novel.

Returning by bus to the farm Fiona reported that Edwin seemed more relaxed than four hours previously. The next morning, despite being wet with perspiration, requiring a change of bedclothes and pyjamas following a sponge wash, he was again in a more relaxed state than during the past few days. Traditional bed care was essential: turning the patient, keeping him dry, warm, well ventilated, access to fluids at all times. During the next few days there was a marked improvement. By the time that Fiona needed to return home the profuse sweating, fever, and lack of awareness had passed. Edwin was slowly on the mend, but weakened and very tired.

With the passage of several weeks the farmer regained his strength; the doctor was overjoyed because his first experience of using sulphur drugs had been successful.

One afternoon Iona encouraged her husband to walk with her around the garden, the rick-yard and out into the meadows, for his wasted muscles needed to be used, to rebuild. As they walked slowly around the yard, the cowshed used for milking was being prepared for the four o'clock session. A Jenny Wren hovered over a stone wall, stabbing into the crevices for grubs. In the manner of a hummingbird it hovered, stabbed, moved a few inches then began again. The tiny creature gave such pleasure to the farmer. He noticed too, a pair of pigeons engaged in mutual grooming; as a rat scurried off the muck heap towards a drain he made a mental note to introduce one of the farm cats to the spot for close investigation.

They passed through a gate and into a paddock; the farmer spontaneously flicked open his pen knife and cut through roots of thistles, docks and cowslips. A usual activity for the fastidious cultivator he instinctively wanted to maintain and improve his land. Then the couple were spotted by Trevelyn's horse; he trotted over and made throat and nasal noises by way of indication of his presence. He wanted to hack out and was saying so. Bucking first then shying he cantered around the farmer crabbing, rolling his head, raising his mane flaying his tail as his upper lip peeled back to reveal teeth. Trevelyn could do nothing; with little strength in his limbs and unsettled balance it would be some weeks before the two resumed their instinctive rapport.

Iona picked her moment, then announced that Edwin's father had died six weeks previously and was now buried at Kenwyn. The farmer remained silent, slowly turned and faced south west, just staring at the horizon, in the direction of Cornwall. Upon returning to the farm house they were able to talk openly about the death in front of the children now. The physical exercise had left the farmer weak. It would be clearly be some time before he would regain his full strength. Meanwhile his financial situation had deteriorated to such an extent that many cows had been sold, thus depleting his magnificent herd and reducing the size of the milk cheque. A trip to the bank for discussions was now called for.

It proved easier at the bank than either the farmer or his wife could have hoped for. Fore-Smith talked about the political tensions in Europe. The call for a re-armament policy by Mr Churchill and how if the European dictators with their vile rhetoric were not prevented from achieving their stated goals then there could be tension. Farming would be crucial to Britain's survival especially if a naval blockade was again placed around the islands in an attempt by the dictators of Europe to starve the democracy into submission.

The old money lender wished for Trevelyn and his wife to fight on. It was odd that when Iona had seen him alone he appeared to want to hasten the sale now; he supported them staying in place. The couple were elated as they walked through the city. Trevelyn led his wife into Millets sweet shop where he bought his wife a box of luxury chocolates. Mrs Millets' teenage boy who was present looked the farmer up and down with considerable disapproval.

The youngster was assuming airs and graces due to his attendance at Alienuns, a small private school that only parents in the locality would send their children to. It impacted heavily upon Thurlchester. Outsiders to the city did not venture into its hallowed portals, motto: Phlque Nocki Hill Pilfication. Every child at the institution believed that he was very important, and instinctively saw the gross inadequacy in others and their education. They took themselves very seriously indeed, did not travel or read, yet by the time they finished school apparently they knew enough, London was a far away place they knew little of nor wanted to. Their dislike of outsiders was intense. It was everything and sufficient to be an old Alienuns. This particular teenager had entered as a junior or Scurra, then having turned 11, risen to the Excores. Now in the sixth form he wore a pink armband on the left side of his blazer with the proud words 'Alienuns Excores'. The headmaster's lessons took the school motto as their title; every boy coming under the man's guidance, enjoyed his tutelage throughout his time at Alienuns.

One particular feature of school etiquette was that the headmaster's wife was known as 'The Doxy'. Whenever a boy passed this particular person he was required to bow, and as he looked at the ground say, "Good morning," or "Good afternoon Doxy." It was perhaps why the characters graduating from this particular institution were usually unable to look a person in the eye when addressing them. The couple remarked upon the contrast between children from Aleniuns and their own children who appeared to have much greater depth and civility than them.

Young Ronald Millet was intent upon taking sweets for a fat boy hanging around outside the shop. Millet's education and upbringing seemed to allow him to push himself forward and in front of people he held in disdain. Farmers, they walked in muck, dirtied their hands; they were not sophisticated in young Millet's eyes. He removed sweets and handed them to the rough boy leaning against a window.

The boy who evidently had a hold over Millet was a crude, uncouth type who previously attended a tough council school. Upon leaving he held a succession of unskilled jobs but was adept at making his way. He gained an earlier reputation for carrying a knife but had reasoned that by gathering a retinue around him, persuading them to enforce his will, it was unnecessary to carry a knife himself and risk arrest. His name was Les Feather. As the farmer and his wife left the shop they noticed that Feather's eyes darted quickly in all directions, whilst he simultaneously talked and pushed sweets into his mouth. Clearly in contempt of Millet, the latter was actually in awe of the bully.

The moment had impressed itself upon Trevelyn and his wife. A new generation beginning to assert itself. Times were changing.

The couple returned to the farm, pleased to know they were treading upon their own soil. Restoring Edwin's health would be a priority, ensuring that the Rheumatic Fever did not re-occur. Rebuilding the farm and their financial status would take longer. Thankfully the children were secure at their schools. The Cathedral school had served the boys well. There was not a 'side' to their boys; they were open, devoid of snobbery, natural free-flowing characters; above all they were instinctive countrymen. Quite a contrast to young Millet.

CHAPTER XII

The news from Europe was continually bad, with talk of war. The previous summer Iona's sister Fiona had travelled around Germany and whilst in Nuremberg watched the charismatic leader Adolf Hitler speak. Seeing him and the other leaders of Germany was terrifying. The description that she gave to her family was now percolating through the British press. A politician named Winston Churchill gave continual warnings regarding the events unfolding around continental Europe. The newspapers owned by Maxwell Aitkin carried warning articles that were impressive in content yet derided by the political establishment in Britain. Then Edwin's sister Charlotte sent by post press cuttings that she had received from her husband in Burma. It appeared that Churchill's fears were even stronger where they appeared in newspapers published around the British Empire.

Trevelyn found it very curious indeed that only twenty years previously a terrible war, 'the war to end all wars' they said, had concluded, following a crazed grab for other people's countries, backed up with terrible new fighting techniques. Yet here were explanations of a potential future war, run by dictators with even deadlier killing devices to hand who did not respect other human beings right to live at all; but the knowledge of what was really going on in Europe with their actual intentions was denied to the British people. Here was the world's foremost democracy hiding from its own population the truth about Europe; but why? who benefited?

As Trevelyn's strength increased, greatly assisted by his wife's cooking and nursing, he was able to again take on the milking and slowly engage in the heavier work on the farm.

He decided to re-build his enterprise by purchasing another bull for his own uses and for hire. His milking herd would gradually be increased, one-by-one and the following year would see the farm utilising all of its available land again. Christmas and New Year would be the end of his unwanted sustained rest.

*   *   *

1939 began as it would end, marked by sheer hard work. The twice daily milking routine, tending to pigs and assisting Iona with any heavy work around the poultry houses. They fully planted the acreage: grass for hay, wheat, barley and oats; clover, kale and turnips and swede for animal feed. Certain fields that were left fallow had poultry turned out upon them. Later in the year, before autumn ploughing the pigs would be given an opportunity to rootle up some arable land.

By May it was necessary to hire another man. Jim Thossell lived in the village and needed a change of farm; he was chosen as an all rounder.

It was also the time that Ruth left the nest. At the instigation of Ruth, Iona had written to her former matron still in Nottingham hospital, enquiring regarding trainee nursing vacancies. Upon receipt of her letter the matron wrote back immediately and said she would take any number of McNiven girls; were there any more?

One spring day, a man in his 30's, the son of a local farmer, knocked upon the door. Heather the youngest answered. It was Caleb Trenwith. He announced: "A' come to see the mister!" The girl replied that her father was now working several fields away and not back until four o'clock milking, could she assist? "Well it's about a sensitive sort of matter missy," announced the man. He paused and rather stared at the girl. There was a certain mystery to the enquiry. "I can take a message for my father."

The man looked stunned, his mouth open, saliva connected his top lip to the bottom; he gulped. "It's too, er sensitive missy; important farming business you will understand." The man was wearing high wellington boots which met a brown sack-coloured coat held together with string. He pushed up at his cap, pulled it down, frowned, ran his fingers under his cap into a line of sweaty hair. "Her ummm missy, it's a tricky sort of business this farmin' business," he said and whistled, no particular tune but it gave to him a few seconds to look away from the girl. "Can you outline the nature of your enquiry Mr Trenwith?" enquired Heather. The man now stood on one foot, began hopping to retain his balance, blew, whistled, became puce in the face then unaccountably gripped his privates with one hand causing a squeal, then loss of balance as he stood upon the foot that had not left the ground.

His expression of considerable pain increased as he appeared to squeeze himself, ever harder. Just then Iona Trevelyn appeared at the door to investigate the fuss. "What is going on" she enquired of both parties. The farmer exhaled, now appearing exhausted he explained, "A matter of such delicacy; only the mister can discuss it." Iona knew immediately what he wanted. "Mr Trenwith this girl is a country girl, she has witnessed birth, death, conception and every stage in between, are you wishing to hire the services of Mr Trevelyn's bull? If so, just say so."

"Yes ma'am I am," said the relieved farmer. "Then come inside have a cup of tea, relax and Mr Trevelyn will be in for his tea shortly before the four o'clock milking." The farmer was relieved; despite his social shyness he did relax into a kitchen chair; sharing a pot of tea he ranged loquaciously over a number of subjects. Breaking the ice with the man drew forth a character usually missed, of considerable knowledge and depth, but quite unable to initiate a conversation. He would make an honest girl a fine husband. She would need a little patience though.

Following the afternoon cup of tea Iona usually accompanied her husband to the fields, he to rouse the cattle with his distinctive calling of their names, causing them to follow a well worn line through fields to the yard and the milking house, she to collect feed for the poultry. Walking through the yard, passing a mounting block for horses with a surface of about four feet square, they noticed it was scattered with empty snail shells. The pair of thrushes often seen around the yard had been busy providing for their brood. Edwin and Iona passed beyond the rick-yard where she picked up a long wooden spoon. Entering the smaller yard geese waited expectantly; a gander moved behind the woman, took a large peck at her buttock and squawked; she turned, banged the bird upon the head leaving it stunned but still on its feet. The ritual occurred most afternoons, as the creature evidently felt threatened. Incredibly, Trevelyn himself was similarly attacked by the stag, or tom turkey. If he strayed within chasing and pecking distance of the 28-pound mature Bronze turkey his backside and upper legs were in danger of being pecked. Further the jealous partner of several hundred hens was not averse to lunging itself from the front, between the man's legs, pecking as he did so. The joys of living with animals!

Thurlchester market was bustling now, as talk of political troubles in Europe gained momentum. The government would need the use of, and cooperation from farmers. Trevelyn genuinely enjoyed his twice monthly market day plus a lunchtime drink at the Market Tavern, contrasting and comparing his efforts and intentions with those of others. Being an acknowledged stockman his company was often sought, like his father before him. He bought and sold from the pens but sometimes just stood with others making observation, mentally rejecting or accepting the stock. The man exuded an authority with his trademark black bowler hat, breeches, leggings, black leather boots, waistcoat with a chain attached to his watch. His face showed calm determined openness. There were many around the city prepared to point out the risks and faults of another man's business, but it was something else to actually take the risk themselves. Few critics had the spirit but Trevelyn had always been prepared to take the risk.

The market place lunchtime exchanges, (often accompanied by a Shepherd's Pie in the winter), were a valuable social intercourse. The best public houses were those where the staff broke most of the glasses.

Thurlchester Market Tavern was run along strict lines. The landlord Wally Remington and his wife entertained the widest selection of farming people, agents, millers, trades people, solicitors and the odd churchman from St Oswolds's Cathedral.

The current bishop, the very reverend Montague Fitz-William kept a selection of red and black Shropshire pigs. Being a younger son of a titled family who had produced four sons, the eldest inherited the estate and farm, following military service; another was a naval officer; one studied law and the last one given by the family to God. It was often the way.

So many of the clergy stretching back centuries were very well educated, talented in fields beyond divinity. Classicists perhaps who translated great works. Writers on every conceivable subject, inventors, scientists, biologists.

Trevelyn's ancestor Malachi, a Cornish rector, had even assisted at the Royal Observatory amongst other efforts. The farmer and the cleric had an easy rapport as they shared Thurlchester's brewery products, including Henry Polak's Ales, of a bitter variety, whilst in conversation about pig-keeping or similar.

For the bishop there was a sense of frustration at not inheriting the estate farm. He would have prospered with his natural innovation and love of stock. Despite being a genuflecting priest his kind were not like professional priests. Without analysis or precondition he trusted the word that he had sworn to accept and explain through something called faith; hearing a still small voice. A genuine Christian mission with high sense of duty yet humility, combined with common sense derived from the Holy Bible. His explanations of human passions and how they often conflict with a divine will were of considerable benefit to all who ventured to ask, then took the time and courtesy to listen.

In a political context he would have been above mere party and its partisan recriminations, but thinking and working for the good of his country. His Armistice Sunday services were particularly inspiring. Those who had served without question were dear to his own heart. Men do not always have access to their favoured chosen path in life however; this man certainly did not, but was ideally suited to the path that God had chosen for him.

The Market Tavern was thick with smoke as Trevelyn and Horace

Varley, a farmer from a nearby village, entered. Green stained glass windows both transmitted and dispersed light, moving into coloured shafts, attracting the smoke which moved along and around the beams of light throughout the room. Groups of men stood talking, drinking, chewing tobacco, smoking. The tumbleweed of humanity drifted around; a flotsam and jetsam of society looking for something or other yet without the required initiative when sedated by ale and comforted by tobacco to achieve much in life.

Information was the currency with which to trade in this environment. Half a dozen solicitors were enjoying an anecdote. One who had clearly made a lot of money from a particular client, quoting from Hillaire Belloc said, "He answered as he took his fees, 'There is no cure for this disease.'" They all chuckled; armed with beer, wine or spirits they drank deep, exchanging laughing glances over the top of their glasses. There was an air of cynicism about them. The key to their trade was never to ask a question that they did not know the answer to, if it might rebound. Also knowing the right question to ask as they never knew what others did not know. Framing the question that unlocks the information was a skill.

Trevelyn passed by this group to farmers and other countrymen. Some carrying flat caps, others trilbys, (in Trevelyn's case, a bowler), some wore brown coats buttoned or if the garment was old, tied with twine. Some carried sticks, as though an extension of themselves. The mix of social position, education and experience was about as broad as it was possible to achieve: public school classical scholars to council school chaps who had ceased formal education by age 13. They shared one binding passion: the land and everything emanating from it. A cohesive social mix of diverse backgrounds with a cultural identity. Rather like the village cricket club team that draws in every social strata; the talented sporting bricklayer, Oxbridge vicar, land owner — professionals and tradesmen coming together to play the game. Such natural affinity for and with their fellow man, transcending social background, had probably assisted Britain in avoiding a revolution.

These were men accustomed to best agricultural practice, or seeking it, certainly unrivalled in continental Europe and beyond, other than in countries of the British Empire. They were custodians of a culture that rendered not only food, but the countryside quite uniquely beautiful. They sought no man's custom. Then when these men subjected themselves to a bureaucracy, officialdom or the law, they used to know that without fear or favour the administration would above all be fair. All of which allowed these people to be law abiding and quite at ease with one another. No secret policeman needed to lurk around these corners.

Trevelyn and Varley bought golden pints of bitter beer, then mingled, laughed, exchanged anecdotes asked questions, discussed prices; at times arranging to visit the other's property to look at and share a problem, or view success. The unbreakable bond between man, land and livestock, gently administered by decent laws existed here. How fared Germany, Spain, Italy and Russia?

On his way home Trevelyn called into Millets to buy Iona's favourite chocolates. The young counter jumper, Ronald, barely managed civility, but took the customer's money anyway.

Arriving home, Trevelyn found Iona was tending a sow who had given birth earlier than expected. She was inside the farrowing pen rubbing the sow's back as it was struggling to finish the process. Some of the piglets appeared to be weak. The three younger children were peering over a door very quietly observing the event; a practical biology lesson. Callum was dispatched to find the brandy bottle and a pipette with which to insert a drop of the warming liquid into the piglets' mouths. Events such as animal births usually caused any available children to become a mute audience.

It proved to be a very profitable harvest that last summer before war was declared. Regius Farm had regained some of its former glory, the milking herd were providing a good monthly cheque, farm gate sales too. A small herd of steers was developing and the new bull was also in great demand. They had pigs in sties, some in a deep litter complex in a barn, others in small movable huts around the fields. The range of poultry was complete: ducks, geese, turkeys, guinea fowl, and chickens, all of whom were producing eggs or meat for the table. During the next year it was intended to re-introduce the sheep, the arable land was to be fully planted. Then Iona had an idea. Goats; she wanted to rear goats and milk them; those slaughtered could be sold as table meat; a number of families enjoyed the rich taste of goat flesh, which is not dissimilar to mutton. "No," said Edwin, "Goats, never." He related a disastrous experience of those most peculiar animals that will eat literally everything in sight; creating chaos out of order. The matter was dropped.

War was formally declared as the harvest was brought in. It was very quickly dubbed as 'The Phoney War' as nothing much happened at first. Young Edward Trevelyn joined the army. His father Edwin was livid but there was little that he could do to prevent it. After all, had he not done the same 25 years previously? Happily, a very enjoyable Christmas was shared by all at Regius Farm; with the mortgage being paid comfortably, food upon the table, the Lord had seemingly blessed Trevelyn's household. Edward was already home on leave, very enthusiastic about army life, but he was yet to carry out any really testing missions.

Ruth, granted annual leave, was bubbling away about nursing life and shared many anecdotes about the McNiven family. Her grandmother wanted Iona to dispatch rail freight parcels of fresh poultry and eggs, as she knew many people who would buy oven-ready birds and free range eggs. During the holiday they worked out timetables for taking their produce to Thurlchester Station; the journey would require one change in Birmingham, then via Nottingham to Hucknall Torkard where, due to the reliability and honesty of the railway company, the family could collect their goods, and on time. Within six hours and at minimal cost the day's free range eggs and other farm produce were delivered to happy customers grateful for a taste of the country. This enterprise provided Iona with a guaranteed market and cash flow.

Ruth brought back garments made by her aunt. With materials now in short supply, mend and make-do the order of the day, cleverly woven pieces of material could be turned into an attractive piece with the appearance of a new garment. When a garment was too worn, or shabby to repair it was cut into strips, colours matched and a rag rug created and then backed with Hessian sacking. Or an apron could be created from old curtains or clothes.

Blackout curtains too were made, from dark heavy material, to hide the light of the house from German air raiding missions. First World War army blankets being ideal for this purpose, Trevelyn had retained his, their use latterly as blanket wraps for sick or recovering children who needed to keep warm, were now employed to obscure themselves from the Hun. Knitting wool could be ordered from the village shop or the city emporiums, collected and paid for one or two skeins at a time until a new garment was finished. The click clacking of knitting needles heard on the local bus was usually drowned by a verbal exchange, though the knitter rarely seemed to drop a stitch or forget an anecdote; quite a skill.

A new culture of food was evident as something called 'rationing' was imposed. Two ounces of butter, eight of margarine, flour or sugar, and two ounces of cheese a week per person was now all that was allowed by law. Every home contained a pantry with a marble slab to keep food cool.

Weekly trips to the cinema provided an escape from reality, with sufficient propaganda contained within the film's message to assist in sustaining morale. Joseph Chamberlain, a member of Parliament at the turn of the century, had spoken of the day when every working man should have a pig. A few years before the policy had been for each man to own or rent a few acres, and keep a cow. How these ideas now took hold, with the naval blockade creating a vice-like grip. Now his son Neville would learn the value of his fathers generation being suspicious of all politics that emanate from continental Europe.

Edward and Ruth when on leave excitedly brought home news of their working lives. Charles, Callum and Heather by contrast were still caught up in the routine of school. Callum however wanted to join the Royal Air Force, his teenage bellicosity needed correcting however.

The government introduced British Summer time by moving the clock forward two hours in order to accommodate factory employees who did not experience sufficient daylight, but it affected the poultry, causing them to not want to roost until nearly midnight, by June. Closing the hen houses was carried out around dusk as the birds would then seek the protective environment of the communal roost. With Edwin rising by 5:30 in preparation for morning milking, during the spring and summer the farm had to increase its daily work schedule to 19 hours.

One evening Iona was desperately tired as she carried out her usual round of shutting up the hen coops, dropping a sliding doorway just above a walkway leading from the ground into the house. After dropping the door a bar shaft was slid across to prevent any movement. Following breakfast the next morning after milking was complete, Trevelyn sat his wife down and told her that he had some news that would distress her. One of the hen houses had received a visitor during the night. A fox had pushed up a coop door, entered and killed all of the 125 hens inside. The scene resembled an abattoir: inside and out, feathers, legs, wings, heads and entrails were blowing around. A gruesome, yet bizarre sight. The other hen houses were clearly disturbed, the unusual noise emanating from them indicated nervousness. It would be necessary to clear up the mess before allowing the remaining flock to be released. Not only had they lost the hens, all were laying birds and several dozen eggs a day would not be delivered to the market place. The experience was a stern reminder of the occasional violence of nature.

Human nature can also demonstrate vagaries of its own. Romany gypsies towing caravans behind skewbald and piebald horses would from time to time situate themselves on a verge alongside Trevelyn's fields. Tramps too would find a barn or hovel to sleep for the night. Edwin sometimes spotted one asleep as he prepared for the early morning milking.

All of these characters were harmless, genuine tramping folk; a fraternity not in pursuit of possessions, but a unique definition of freedom. Their lack of desire for consumer goods seemed to instill fear and hostility into people who rejected their advances. Usually they only sought a billycan of fresh water. Buying pegs from the gypsy women or having knives ground by a wheel attached to a bicycle on a strut mount, were the usual reasons for contact. Many had a generosity derived from their inherited devotion to the Bible. They certainly led their lives by an ordained pace rather than a man-made one, tramping in pursuit, observing and absorbing, then sharing their knowledge and lore.

* * *

There is a saying, well-known around the villages of sub-Sahara Africa, which roughly translated states that it only takes a couple to make a baby but that it requires a whole village to bring it up. Other cultures too have similar sayings and beliefs. 1940's Britain was little different in that typically in any village, tuition for music, sport and, hobbies; the scouts, cubs, guides, brownies, and educated societies too, would impact upon a child.

Opportunities for earning pocket money existed for minors still in full-time education. It began the introductory process to the greater outside world, beyond the tight-knit family unit. One of Heather's errands was to deliver eggs and poultry to houses after school and before the evening meal.

It gave her access to a variety of new social and economic circumstances, though some of the characters on the round were not exactly sought after, by the majority of people.

One particular woman who only ever complained, fitted the description by the Reverend John Gaule describing witches as: "Every old woman with a wrinkled face, a hairy lip, a squint eye, a scolding tongue, and a dog or cat by her side." Anyone resembling this was at great risk of being judged a witch. Maud Burbidge unfortunately fitted into that category.

Her brother Cuthbert was not socially acceptable to many either. Maud would always complain about the price and quality of the eggs and poultry, never have money readily available and linger far too long over the simple exercise of exchange of payment for goods. Around her door hung old jam jars with either a little honey or jam and water inside then a lid with holes allowing wasps, flies and other insects into the jar to first gorge upon then drown in the sticky liquid. Hanging upon a rusty nail upside down tied by their legs were usually an assortment of crows, rooks, pigeon and rabbits caught or killed with a catapult by her brother Cuthbert. Elsewhere hung a galvanised iron bath that had not endured too much service.

Cuthbert said odd things, his favourite line, seeing a girl or young woman walking towards the bakery was: "There is a more than yeast arising in a that there bakery youngun, ye be careful to keep a grip of yer knickers now." "Tee, he, he," inevitably followed! As he laughed his gums showed a few peg teeth stained with 'baccie'. His terrible breath cut through the air like a javelin. Cuthbert also kept ferrets inside his shirt, and enjoyed showing them to all.

Another of Heather's deliveries was to the Wardle household where Mr Wardle, a self important man could be heard rowing with his wife from outside the property, even as distant as the garden gate. Opening the door to a knock he was as pleasant as any person could appear to be; solicitous to all. As the door closed the house bully resumed his natural character. That which occurs behind closed doors is known only to the participants. Mrs Wardle did have an outlet though; the Girl Guide Association was her passion. Her troupe had produced three Queen's Guides.

Leonard Smith and his wife bought every week. A character with a continually changing personality he was known as 'The Onion' as yet another layer peeled away. Bunty, his wife, always appeared with curlers in her hair often with a net over it. Their house only ever smelt of fried food and Bubble and Squeak, potatoes, and left over vegetables fried up in a hash — as evidently they lived off the frying pan!

The delivery to an overgrown Victorian house remote from the main village, to Mr Cyril Latimer, was a challenge. There is ironically, rarely a more illiberal even intransigent character; than a very liberal person, who; having imposed his views will tolerate no other point of view. Particularly so in political circles when even despite categorical proof of the failure of his ideas. With Latimer an intolerant narrow-mindedness became evident if the rightness of his thinking came under serious challenge. His purchase of half a dozen eggs occasionally was always welcome, but not his views taken from the editorial of 'The Morning Star' newspaper.

Dr Andrews and his wife were top drawer academics, having lectured within a number of colonial universities. He had a few more years of working life left — before retirement from a brilliant mathematical career of teaching, book and pamphlet writing — with a final job at the Cathedral School. Approaching the back door and glancing through the windows one was struck by the floor-to-ceiling books and papers, though his superb brain could quickly find any specific item upon request.

Their weekly request for fresh farm produce was delivered to a character who opened the door humming or singing, always jovial, and wearing his academic gown, which he used to propel himself by turning the sleeves forward like a child's paddle boat on a municipal lake. He swivelled them backwards to reverse, then turning right; the left sleeve would be rotated forwards, a left turn, vice versa. Occasionally, he exploded into sneezes, exhaling copious quantities of snuff recently self-administered, into a silk handkerchief. He was a noted sight in Thurlchester, cycling along with his wife on high old bicycles, shabby brown leather satchels precariously balanced with wickerwork baskets upon the front, with papers fighting to escape the cramped conditions.

A village shop with access to rationed foodstuffs and therefore guaranteed trade, proffered goods via large hand painted metal sign boards: 'Lyons Tea', 'Canchoo Tea', 'Brooke Bond Tea,' 'Wall's Ice Cream' and 'Craven A' cigarettes with the logo of a black cat. The proprietors could be seen walking to and from a patch of land where they kept stock, bought from Trevelyn, with yokes around their necks; a wooden apparatus which straddled the shoulders, chains hanging from each end holding buckets for water. They sold 'snorkers' or sausages with an indeterminate filling but guaranteed to fill an empty belly. Some of their customers almost ritually bought a tin of fruit for Sunday lunchtime pudding and a tin of salmon for Sunday tea; it never varied within certain households. The shop bought eggs, milk and clotted cream from the farm though, for re-sale.

Visiting the house of Reg Sawford, who had served right through the war of 1914 to 1918, it was essential to keep any conversation superficial. Reg drank too much because of his nightmares born of that experience; his demons could be provoked then released too easily. Tragically his life had been lived upon a knife edge ever since 1918. He enjoyed one outlet away from work: pigeons. His loft was immaculate, being both a fancier and racer of the birds. He won prizes for racing and the condition of his birds.

At Colonel Mabbet's imposing Georgian property the noisy dogs alerted the master of the household to the arrival of a visitor. The character generally appeared with a monocle, which dropped out of his eye as he caught your glance and raised an eyebrow. A flecked red face was graced by a bulbous purple nose. He was alert, businesslike, courteous and quick with his dealings. It usually seemed as though something else was pressing for his return. Rolling boiled sweets around his mouth in order to freshen his breath, meeting him virtually always came with an offer of one of his multi-coloured sweets.

Sometimes, the Colonel asked Heather if her siblings and friends could attend one of his shooting parties as beaters or a point-to-point horse race meeting to carry out assistant steward duties, for extra pocket money. Mabbet, in common with Trevelyn, enjoyed running a pony and trap, plus a range of other country pursuits, and was noticeably visible at the Thurlchester Gymkhana as a judge. A radio aerial hung from a tree by the back door of Mabbet's house, which was attached to a copper rod pushed into the ground, acting as an earthing device; sometimes a gramophone could be heard playing well known pieces of opera.

Another not dissimilar retired man had been a colonial civil servant. Matthew Collingwood MBE was an Arabist-Muslim convert, incredibly well read and well travelled, and pleasantly knowledgeable. His evenings speaking presentations to the Thurlchester Historical Society were notable; similarly he gave stirring talks to the Scouts, Women's Institute and British Legion. Well rounded, ethical, basically decent; in common with many whose lives had been action packed the relative dullness of a retired existence induced an excess of drinking, sending his mind into other worlds. It was definitely not an adherence to the Sufi sect of whirling dervishes that caused him to spin upon his own axis, but secular man-made grog, inducing another quite different intoxication.

Nick Yule would usually be caught being scolded by his wife. The place was untidy, overgrown. Heather had forgotten just how many times she had heard Mrs Yule shouting, "Pulling weeds? You've only ever been good at pulling corks, not weeds." She evidently wished for the garden to be dug and useful vegetables planted.

However, they bought two dozen eggs weekly and occasionally an oven-ready chicken; it all assisted the Trevelyn exchequer. Gradually, the farmer prospered again following the government call to 'Dig for Britain' which followed a naval and submarine blockade of the British Isles. There were too few hours in the day, or enough available hands to assist. Charles had joined the army; Callum was ready to join the air force. The farmhouse employed Josie Upcroft and five men outside, none of whom were able or fit for military service. All able men were in uniform, sent to the mines, or employed in war work somehow.

Parliament was the national forum; its proceedings faithfully recorded by the serious press, and Hansard (transcripts of the proceedings of the Legislative Assembly), available within the library a few days later showed the way. Its authority carried throughout the British Isles. Prime Minister Neville Chamberlain had entered the House for a debate regarding the defeat of Norway to the National Socialists upright and alert, but left the House crumpled, bent due to a verbal pounding from many, including David Lloyd George and Leopold Amery. He was suddenly, within an hour or two, a broken man, as all parties looked to Lord Halifax and Winston Churchill; the latter being asked to form a coalition administration.

Whatever the governments did they were denigrated by Aneurin Bevan. Trevelyn called him 'Urinal Bevan', his refrain, "That so-and-so has the lucidity of a fundamentally sterile mind," gained him near mythical status in Ebbw Vale and throughout the Labour movement, as he sought the imposition of the opposite sort of socialism to that now at war with Britain.

Life in the village went on though; the cricket club still played, with youngsters and men over forty. Public house life was sometimes raucous, with rat fights if a couple of males were caught. or cock fights after hours, for the discreet and select few to bet upon. Billiards games against neighbouring villages; darts or ring and hook — throwing a metal ring 12 feet or so onto a hook, in competition. Together with various improvised games using horseshoes, bowls and items attached to string, entertainment was always available, mostly homemade.

One man, Jimmy Berry, had possessed a good voice as a youngster and gave solo performances in the church choir. Like Bo Jangles Robinson, the New Orleans dancer and entertainer, he now drank then performed, which produced thirst with adrenalin causing the need to perform again. He responded to drinks and tips whilst the alcohol gradually destroyed his physique and mental capacities. The public bar was however his only stage now, whilst his wife gave piano lessons from the front parlour to generations of children, thus supplementing the housekeeping.

The bureaucracy tightened its grip, paperwork and inspections abounded. Upon the birth of pigs or calves the authorities had to be informed. Now Police attended sheep dipping. For those who killed an animal, say a pig, their meat ration would have to be given up for a year. People were not allowed to kill lambs. Trevelyn was hit by this. Henry Saxon the village butcher was 'on side'. He and Trevelyn found suitable times to meet upon the farm. Bringing the tools of his abattoir trade Saxon would kill a pig when there was an 'R' in the month, otherwise it was too hot, and share the meat with the farmer. It meant, however under-declaring the birth rate of these animals. Eight piglets survived of the nine born! A jail sentence awaited those who were caught; which many were. With the ongoing problem of empty bellies, Hitler and his German government had much to answer for.

The German leader had written a book setting out his plans for Europe, and how they should be achieved. Typical of the undemocratic fanatics associated with European politics he wrote: "The broad mass of a nation will more easily fall victim to a big lie than a smaller one. The greater the lie, the greater the chance that it will be believed."

His SS General Reinhard Heydrich, a very cruel soldier, produced terrible plans explained within his own book 'The Reich Plan for the

Domination of Europe' involving the military suppression of Europe with mass extermination, genocide and a cleansing of unwanted people. Czechoslovakia was his proving ground.

Then, even more worrying for those who would be left after the war was the book titled 'European Economic Community' published in 1942, written by Dr Walther Funk, President of Germany's Reichsbank, and Minister of the Economy. Along with leading German industrialists, Hitler's Finance Minister produced his blueprint for governing Europe after the current hot war was over.

The European Economic Community would have trans-European networks, common agricultural policies, common trade, industrial and single monetary policies, with a Europabank and common currency controlled by Germany. The portent for the future was dire indeed. As Trevelyn and others discussed the war and their own future within Britain, whether in village or city, everyone agreed that no patriotic British government would ever sign up for these European ideas of control — but the ongoing war was far from won.

The transparent plans for producing cooperative regional governments throughout Europe similar to that in Vichy, France, would clearly fail in Britain. Paying British taxes into a German dominated European federal state — a European Union of States of countries that were once independent, sovereign and free, using unelected regional assemblies — was the classic way to divide and rule. Further, the Nazi German usage of the occult as an instrument of control, particularly within their training methods, would instinctively create turmoil, revulsion, followed by rejection. Violent repulsion might occur as adherants' lives spun out of control. The Conservative and Unionist Party for one, always calling for King and country, stressing duty and patriotism would never succumb to that idea. The Anglican communion, sometimes mockingly referred to as 'the Tory party at prayer' would see through it.

All of the powerful trade unions who also controlled the Labour and Cooperative Party through financing would never be so naïve as to be tricked by the ideas put forward by Walther Funk and the German Government. Their primary concern was British jobs. However, first it was necessary to actually win the war, rid the world and Europe of the undemocratic dictators in order to secure Britain as an independent entity, truly safe with its unique constitutional practice; Magna Carta, Habeus Corpus, Common Law, Declaration of Rights, Declaration of Arbroath and its system of parliamentary reform acts; together with a free press and independent judiciary.

Many people did however find it strange that the current Prime Minister, Mr Churchill, was suppressed from expressing his views during the 1930's regarding the European dictator's intentions. Further, the Conservative and Unionist Party tried to de-select him from his parliamentary seat, then the BBC (British Broadcasting Corporation) would not allow him to speak over the airwaves. Trevelyn and many others gained accurate knowledge of exactly what was going on in Europe from family members throughout the British Empire, who were cutting out and posting relevant press articles to them.

There were certainly strange inconsistencies, unexplained and evidently suppressed by the internal British media. As people talked they wondered if the same odd attitude towards an earlier European dictator, Napoleon Bonaparte, had existed. After all the Frenchman had been responsible for two million deaths, perhaps even three million.

During a conversation at Thurlchester market the Bishop, breaking with his fascination for pigs and joining in with a philosophical conversation regarding the war referred to the great Aristotle, who in Athens over 300 years BC had written: "The society that loses its grip on the past is in danger, for it produces men who know nothing but the present, and who are not aware that life has been and could be different from what it is. Such men bear tyranny easily, for they have nothing with which to compare it."

Farming people were very knowledgeable regarding the past. They knew that learning from past experience taught them how to produce food in any given soil or climatic circumstance. In any context the more knowledge of the past that was gleaned, the more contemporary human beings knew how to plan for the future. Farming had since the ancient world followed the pastoral method shared by the writer Virgil within his treatise 'The Georgics'. Correct treatment of the land, best practice all around drew its inspiration from proven custom. Revolutionary practice may upset the rhythms of nature, both in connection with the land and governance of the population who relied upon that land to eat.

Joseph Stalin in Russia and others of his ilk were destroying centuries of good agrarian practice and causing a politically driven man-made famine, destroying spirit and land management which had evolved through recorded history. At least the British government by comparison had minimal bureaucrats and now inspired its farming sector with: "Dig for Britain!" A farmer had recognisable status; respect for the man who gainfully produced good crop yields that fed the country at minimal price had a better result than a brutalising military backed by a corrupt bureaucracy who stole the farmer's crops and starved his family, shooting any dissenters. Ideology and farming never did mix; the master plan of Dr Walther Funk and his common agricultural policy could only fail.

Providing the British military could do its job the madness of the plan for European Integration under Germany after its hot war could never be imposed upon the British Isles. Throughout and around Eatonville plots of land were dug for potatoes, mangle wurzels, swede, turnips — as feed for cattle and humans alike. A surprising number of grass verges, triangles of unused land, former headlands or wasteland, were found to be ideal for cultivation. Never was the village show and church fete so well patronised by many aspirant horticulturalists of all ages. Three generations in cooperation to produce food.

Wine production reached a peak during the war. Never mind the 'Appellation Controlee', (French regulations for insuring quality local wines), the rural palette minded little if the hooch was derived from elderberry, blackberry, carrot or tea dregs, it would all produce drinkable wine. Rumours had it that even potheen, (an illegal whisky distilled from potatoes, notably in the west of Ireland, Aran Islands and other remote places), was being produced.

The war gave Thurlchester a new vibrancy, with so many young and eligible people socializing during their time off duty. The Royal Air Force and the army had bases sufficiently close to bus in service people who patronised the numerous public houses, and dances at the Commemoration Hall. The magnificent structure built to commemorate Queen Victoria's Diamond Jubilee in 1897, could accommodate 500 people, with a big band emulating Major Glenn Miller's orchestra. BBC radio was playing Miller's intoxicating music regularly, causing touring bands to be requested to play similar popular tunes.

Those who had arrived via the Thurlchester train wanted to hear the 'Chattanooga Choo Choo'. Jazz sessions offered renderings of music composed by famous American musicians known as 'The Count, The Duke and the Earl' the gyrating rhythms of ragtime synonymous with America's deep south and the bands associated with Basie, Ellington, Heinz, and Louis Armstrong too. Couples paired off quickly, their body language indicating the moment when liking turned to love, perhaps even consummated, primarily by individuals who knew they might be dead tomorrow. Observation of that was a subjective concept though.

Humour remained, poking fun at authority, as Messrs Gilbert and Sullivan's operettas were performed by the Thurlchester Operatic Society. Written at a time when Britain was the most powerful country in the world, yet here were characters sticking two fingers up at authority, satirising everything; a well known stationer and member of Parliament, Mr. W.H. Smith, included. "I am the very model of a modern major general. . ." was sung as a reflected tease of their own commanding officers, by the troops. No country had ever allowed such irreverence with self deprecation. It reflected moral certainties, security of the governing classes, essentially the relaxed nature of society.

Young people in uniform had money in their pockets, factory staff too, especially with all of the available overtime. There was little to spend the money on due to rationing but alcohol was plentiful though the government heavily taxed it, clawing back as quickly as was possible what had been paid out in the form of a salary or wage. Nobody thought to ask the question as to why intoxicating a nation thus anesthetising its sensibilities was quite so useful to government. They could ask fewer questions now of course, security saw to it.

Conversations within the Eaton Alms however were much happier than in the greater world beyond. Due in part to a certain tobacco grown and shared by 'Old Brum' — a character so named because his unknown father had originated from Birmingham. Maybe a drover passing by. Catlike, he impregnated a local female then slunk off never to be heard of again, other than through anecdote. Old Brum's mother had suffered the indignation of all 'naughty' or 'fallen' women. Sadly for mother and son no man took them on; she struggled until an early death in her 40's. 'Old Brum however was adept at growing tobacco which he cut at harvest, dried by tying and hanging in bundles, soaking in brandy then leaving to cure before cutting into pieces for chewing, rolling or filling pipes with.

Some men chewed and smoked the tobacco simultaneously. They would spit great mouthfuls of the stuff, ideally several feet away from their person. Old Brum rolled his tobacco, then filled a clay pipe taking seemingly endless time and effort, in the same way that shepherds of goat and sheep flocks within Levantine countries do. Meticulously and so patiently preparing their tobacco for smoking over many minutes, whilst watching their charges; finally, with the piece of art ready for actually placing into his mouth and lighting; then, as though playing a reed instrument an embrachure would be formed, between mouth, pipe or cigarette and air, somehow all in unison to produce a certain satisfaction. Old Brum and Middle Eastern shepherds alike thus satisfied a craving.

A man called Greene from a large interrelated family in Eatonville was born with a hair lip. He had perfected a way of gobbing lengths of unwanted chewed tobacco several feet in a line through the imperfection in his upper lip, then refilling the orifice with a rolled cigarette.

The damp of his cavernous skin held any cigarette firm, such that it rode the movements of his upper lip as he spoke. It was however important that he observed the closeness of this burning item so as not to lose the skin from his upper lip. He could spit the butt away as though a dart however, when the moment came.

The tobacco nurtured and cured by Old Brum, along with the wine-making and sharing of vegetable growing and smallholding activity made life palatable for the village folk. A private life away from the gaze of the state. No excise man or town council would dare venture here into this corner of private life.

Britain had traditionally been a country of instinctive order with minimal law; respect and regard for it and those sworn to uphold it was therefore natural. The streets were safe; crime was kept to a minimum due to a visible active uniformed police presence. Police night-time patrols brought the law into close and direct contact with those it sought to protect and its potential adversaries.

The night-time 'Beat' constable 'shaking hands with door knobs,' trying every potential entry or exit point to properties around the village or town during his shift had no equal for discovering burglary. Making notes in a handbook regarding those seen upon the street, stopping or searching known or likely miscreants then reporting everything to the collator's office at the police station before going home ensured that riff raff were correctly monitored by intelligence gathering. Pickpockets, 'Billy the Dip' seen within the marketplace or at the races may be noticed spending excessive cash within a public house on the beat; from where did he obtain his cash, given his lack of conventional working practices? A grateful public would often quietly leave some fresh garden produce upon the constable's doorstep, gratitude for a benign approach to maintaining the King's peace. God save the King.

Yet, one intuitive desire to belong, not political but inarticulate patriotism, was shared by all those in the home guard. Men, and adolescents not even yet men, clambered to join, take part, prepare, stay fit, get fit; fight the totalitarian national socialist enemy. The Europe that for centuries had one way or another tried to rob British forebears of their hard won freedom by stealing their islands, was omnipresent. Had not those forebears cut a bow from hazel, arrows from yew, met by the church lytch gate to then occupy common ground to practice and perfect as archers and long bowmen? This is now remembered every St Crispin's Day as the anniversary of a battle called Agincourt. Their earlier sacrifice would, if necessary, also be the home guards' sacrifice.

Then, appreciating that sacrifice became possible for Edwin and Iona Trevelyn. Their fourth child, Callum, born in 1925, joined the Royal Air Force, becoming a bomber aircraft pilot. On the 2nd of April 1945, Iona was plagued by a robin hopping around her. It flew with her when she collected the eggs; as she fed the various poultry and returned to the house it squawked a peculiar noise; disconcerting, unnerving. Invoking country lore she was stirred. The following day a telegram arrived from the Ministry of War, the following week confirmation along with letters, personal effects and a series of photographs taken during a funeral of nine airmen near Jerusalem in the Holy Land. The one son who above all things wanted to farm, continuing the tradition, was dead. A most dreadful melancholy descended upon the farm. Walking through the fields during the ensuing days, tending poultry twice daily, Iona's mind played over and over Samuel Barber's 'Adagio for Strings'. An increasingly popular orchestral piece, its poignancy just right for this moment in time, scoring into her mind its unique melancholy which reflected hers at the loss of that son. A few days later Charlotte arrived from Cornwall to commiserate with Iona; she too had lost her eldest son Matthew, killed in Burma, and needed the company of a mother in similar circumstances. Charlotte was now quite different in approach to Iona now. Ever the show off, extrovert, centre of attention, good conversationalist, that had evaporated in gloom. The bereaved mothers now found communication easy , yet in a uniquely private way.

A few weeks later Martha drove to Eatonville from Truro and spent a while with the family. She too had changed in her attitude towards Iona, only looking for ways in which to commiserate, as the war ended.

*   *   *

With Edward Trevelyn now demobilized from the services and working upon the farm, an army pal Duncan Forbes turned up one day, showing off his noisy red sports car. Forbes crammed in Edward and his youngest sister Heather for spin around the country lanes. Having taken the girl off in such a flourish Aunt Martha, (visiting again), was quite appalled, turning to her brother she called, "Edwin, the girl will be ruined; her reputation left in tatters. You must do something." Taking her only brother aside she remonstrated with him for allowing such informality.

Trevelyn explained how a lack of reverence did now exist. Ruth too was changed by her nursing experience along with her boyfriend, a doctor; they were each given to far less formality in dealings with their fellow man than people would have expected before the war. It confused and worried Martha. "where will it all end?" she asked. When the exuberant threesome returned from their driving Martha thought that she detected alcohol upon their breath.

Apoplectic, wanting a showdown, before it was possible to gather everyone to hear her piece the three had disappeared into the fields with a gun. Apparently Edward wanted to show to Forbes his 12-bore shotgun. Heather sought involvement in the fun. Off they went. Martha watched their progress from the three sitting room windows until all sight of them was lost. Then she fled the house in pursuit crying, "She is ruined Edwin. Mark my words the girl is ruined!" In pursuit of the three adventurers Martha encountered ruts of dried mud which caused her to overbalance into a bank of stinging nettles. Now sitting upon her legs and hands unable to continue any further she slowly and very angrily made her way back to the farmhouse, muttering. Frustrated by her failure to confront irreverent behaviour she decided to bide her time.

Forbes was invited for tea. There had been a day of much jollity; the fun spilled over into the dining room. Impious attitudes still abounded, the young men were free of the war and military life with its associated constrictions. Heather was home from her technical drawing course in London; frivolity was the order of the day. When the subject of the red sports car was raised Forbes told of journeys made, despite petrol rationing. He mentioned one trip to Cornwall. Martha sat up, wide-eyed periscope-like, awaiting something. Forbes told the assembled party about his experiences in Cornwall, adding that he did not wish to return because he found the people "Narrow-minded, chapel-going Cornish folk; not to my liking."

Heather gulped. Iona and Trevelyn looked at Martha who abruptly sat even more upright and rigid. Placing both of her hands flat upon the dining room table either side of her plate, now goggle-eyed, looking generally across the table at no person in particular she drew breath slowly then announced in a quivering yet angry voice, "Ii amm aa narrow minded chapel going Cornishwoman, but you young man are an insolent discourteous and presumptive character of poor breeding," she finished, and inhaled deeply.

Edward broke the silence. "Duncan, please, it's time." The two younger men rushed out of the now silent room; within seconds the sports car fired into life, soft voices were heard as Forbes let out the clutch abruptly. The last that the assembled party was aware of was the skidding back wheels of the car throwing gravel stones back at the door. Duncan Forbes had left. Yet his impression would linger. So many diverse characters both friends and family arrived at the farm, some unexpectedly, wishing for an impromptu holiday. Fraser McNiven was one such person. Unannounced, or either side of a telegram, he had chosen a moment that suited him to socialise. Not one to consider too deeply the concerns of others he alighted from a taxi with his golf clubs for use upon Thurlchester Golf Links, and his fishing tackle with which to pursue his favoured Pike among the reeds of the River Kells, thus combining his two interests. He had always been something of a disruptive influence upon the boys during his stays upon the farm.

Yet another maverick who usually even neglected to telegram, and up from Cornwall, was cousin Humphrey. Needing first a deep chair then a respectful mute audience, a bottle of gin, a glass within arm's reach, he lingered, talking at length about his recent projects wasting much time; it was odd how little interest he took in the affairs of his hosts.

However, it is your friends that you choose, but respectfully accept your family. Trevelyn was actually aware that the lucrative markets built during wartime were not necessarily strong everlasting relationships. The German naval and submarine blockade concentrated minds upon finding and obtaining local produce. History tends to repeat itself in so many respects. After the 1914 – 1918 war British markets were quickly dissipated as imports flowed in from America and Australia. The former colonies having the economy of scale to their advantage. It was mechanisation that Trevelyn saw as his ultimate saving. Labour was expensive, not always reliable. Already the internal combustion engine was changing villages. Deliveries could now be from not only Thurlchester but using rail or road transport, from almost anywhere.

Milking was developing from a hand operation into a mechanical process. Harvesting of hay and the numerous corn crops too were increasingly involving subcontractors, calling in with their specialist machinery to assist, before moving on to the next farm. The pace of change was gathering momentum as Trevelyn and his son decided to buy their first tractor. A secondhand Ferguson, with various devices and attachments, allowing the vehicle to perform many tasks. Ploughing, harrowing, ring rolling, carrying a load with its own trailer box, the gun metal grey tractor was of the right proportion to be serviceable around small holdings, agricultural and horticultural enterprises too. Using hydraulic engineering it cleverly became a machine for all seasons.

Having bought the tractor at a sale, transported it by rail to Thurlchester thence under its own power to the farm, word quickly spread that Eatonville had its first tractor, the 'Fergie'. Numerous young men arrived that day to inspect the machine. Giving a false impression of great wisdom they walked around the vehicle some with hands in pockets, nodding, commenting, and kicking the tyres as though that action conveyed intimate knowledge of some sort. Later within the Eaton Alms the tractor became a talking point. It was strange how certain men, despite little or no understanding of tractors elevated themselves to positions of great knowledge. The farm had made its first big post-war change; turning away from human labour.

Nature however did not change in the same way; the early lambs always produced an orphan, or one that for some reason was rejected by its mother. It, or they, would be hand-reared, bottle-fed as though a baby. Quite a novelty for a while, having a lamb then sheep following you everywhere, but eventually it could test one's patience. Then as the Spring progressed Swallows, Martins and Swifts arrived with piercing screeches, dived at the mud near to the edge of puddles scooping up a beakful for nest building material, and reoccupied the milking parlour, pig sties and other buildings for a short lease. Repairing earlier nests for the current years breeding, their gathering upon the telegraph wires in lines was an early indication of the onset of Autumn.

Rural evolution forced by government dictate saw the dispossession of 4,000 farmers who would not comply with factory farming; destruction of hedges, woodlands, ponds and the beautiful scenery. Agricultural 'units' of industrial scale were now in vogue. As families were driven away from the land social cohesion was undermined; lost and disposed country people took to alcohol, even drugs, their spirit broken.

By contrast, Norway, particularly in the mountainous and beautiful west, (composer Edward Greig's country), of waterfalls, crags and tiny holdings of perhaps 20 acres, working under difficult circumstances, where cutting grass for hay up to five times during a very short summer season was quite usual, created a legal framework wherein farmers could make a living from the land and remain upon a family farm. This far-sighted policy ensured that an entire culture and way of life was profitable, preserved and then inherited.

Seeing changes occur around the farmyard, with new buildings and upon the land, triggered Iona to instigate a change of her own. A vehicle that usually transported sheep arrived one day with eight four-legged animals who Trevelyn did not wish to make the acquaintance of. Goats had held a fascination for Iona since she began her farming and married life. Despite her husband's reservations, indeed refusal to countenance the subject of goats, Iona had bought seven nannies and a billygoat.

As Trevelyn predicted disaster followed, together with rows. The stupid animals managed to burrow into everything, and go literally everywhere — the scullery, milk parlour, garden, orchard and the meal barn. Everywhere they went defecation occurred, even in the farmhouse, where such wily creatures as the cats knew that even they had no access.

Despite the goats' milk yield, with another potential market, those people suffering with Eczema, Asthma or Psoriasis would readily buy the product. Cheese produced from goats' milk was an acquired taste; a butcher in Thurlchester could sell it though. Then disaster did strike. Josie Upcroft had placed upon various lines much farm washing; towels from the milking parlour, together with house washing too. The goats spotted the activity, somehow nosed open the garden gate, then walking down the line of washing chewed off whatever they could reach. Trevelyn had become accustomed to wearing 'long johns', pants of thick warm brushed cotton. The goats chewed off the legs, reducing the garments to shorts. Damage was carried out to other items as well. That evening Iona picked her moment after the meal to deliver the news to her husband. Barely able to contain her giggles she finally held up her husband's now smaller clothing items, turning them first one way then the other, announcing that it was just as well that Edwin's backside was not within the garment when the goats struck! He did not see the funny side of the incident, though she could now barely contain her laughter. He walked out announcing an unscheduled visit to see Ken Polgreen. His mood was dark. She now roared with laughter finding her own defiance so funny. Yet he was right; goats were a problem.

The following morning after milking and breakfast Iona opened the kitchen door to Ken Polgreen who announced that he was there to collect the goats. A rather strange conversation took place as a delighted Trevelyn appeared, now smiling, laughing, wanting to assist the publican with the addition to his smallholding. Iona was open mouthed hissing at events that were now unfolding out of her control. Polgreen gave the farmer cash for the animals; after deducting some for the purchase of replacement clothes he then gave the remainder to his wife telling her to henceforth confine herself to poultry The two men then proceeded to corral the goats before driving them on foot to the land attached to the public house. The publican very quickly had to endure jokes about the white beer on sale and its lack of potency!

With the closure of wartime local military installations the publican needed to replace the trade not now entering his establishment with several other forms of income. His pigs, geese, hens and now goats from Trevelyn all assisted him with balancing his books. The war was dreadful, bringing with it much sadness but it also brought work and income. Small wartime airfields and army training centres were superfluous as the North Atlantic Treaty Organisation and Mr Churchill's description of the 'Iron Curtain' occupied the minds of military planners. Eatonville and Thurlchester now had to forget the armed services providing ready customers. Agriculture and everything supporting or sustaining it required nurturing if the sector was to maintain its position; surely British governments would do everything possible to assist.

Farming as a way of life affected many more villagers than those directly employed within the industry. It exposed a village community to nature and nurture, the natural world and the necessary respect for 'our shared environment'. Corporations, on the other hand distanced the general population from the land as they created factory farms with wealthy, sometimes dubious accountants and lawyers, deriving the highest salaries as they nurtured paperwork.

Electricity and its easy availability throughout the farm premises had made life much easier. People could switch on lights, enabling them to comfortably walk everywhere into barns and around yards. Activity therefore continued safely well into the evening, or throughout the night if an animal chose to give birth then.

The oil generator installed very many years previously was now worn out. Mains power was available so with a view to converting, Trevelyn approached the nationalised supplier, who told him that only their approved electricians were acceptable to carry out the necessary work. It was indeed a closed shop. Obtaining quotations from those approved by the Electricity Board and local independent self-employed men, the farmer noticed a huge discrepancy in prices. The independent man who worked long hours, was less precious, needing fewer statutory breaks yet far cheaper and quicker whilst having a sense of humour too. The Electricity Board clones were oblivious to the concept of serving customers, and whose money they sought. They thought only of their rights.

Following the work being finished a certificate of acceptable completion was necessary before the Board would connect the farm to the national grid. When the inspector called to tick off the work he asked for the identity of the tradesman who carried out the work, and his union number too. Trevelyn refused. There was a row. The inspector left. When Trevelyn contacted the Board they only wanted to know the identity of the tradesman. Again Trevelyn refused. Now, with the generator gone, there was no electrical power. The family used candles within the house, cooked with gas, not mains though, carrying oil lamps within the milking sheds and elsewhere around the farm, as the stand-off continued.

Autumn of 1946 gave way to a severe winter; deep snow, very cold with hard frosts, naturally followed by floods. Cast iron stand pipes were in use for many weeks as houses were frozen; carrying water in for everything, both household and stock, which tested the stamina of even the strongest. The internal farmhouse windows had been frosted since before Christmas displaying those magnificent designs of nature that provided inspiration for lacemaking, curtains; tablecloths, lingerie, anti-Macassars too — those so essential chairback protectors from men's all pervading hair Macassar Oil. Perhaps only Hedge Parsley, known as Keck, or Queen Anne's Lace could match the inspiration of frost for a design patten; ironically, neither item was particularly welcome, ice within the farmhouse or Keck in the fields.

Every time Trevelyn rang the Electricity Board for an inspection all they wished to know was the identity of the tradesman. The electrician's livelihood was in danger of being denied to him; given the problems associated with circumventing the maintenance of a closed shop Trevelyn had to keep it secret. By March the severity of the winter had been sufficient to trouble the record books and their keepers. The Electricity Board inspector turned up unannounced one afternoon. He wished to converse with Iona. Following that, the man found Trevelyn inside an animal barn. He began asking regarding the details of the electrical contractor, as Trevelyn talked about stock, current affairs, the rugby results, indeed anything except electricity.

Throughout the afternoon the inspector followed Trevelyn around the farmyards. At one point the farmer indicated the presence of a cat; anticipating milking time and a squirt of warm milk it was busily engaged

cleaning its back end, one leg in the air, as all cats take a certain stance
when thus occupied. "Look," said Trevelyn, "my farm cats play the cello,
what beautiful music." Indeed the animal was seemingly working at
strings in a stance identical to a cello player. The inspector was not amused.
He walked with Trevelyn into the fields as he summoned the cattle for
milking, carried out that task and returned the cows to their pasture. All
of the time he asked, "Who was the contractor?" For hours the two men
sparred, as the pigs were fed, sheep tended to, milking machinery washed
and cleaned ready for the following morning. "Who was your contractor,
what is his name?" queried the inspector as Trevelyn found yet another
subject from his broad repertoire with which to interest the man away from
his monotonous incantation.

Finally, the inspector said, "Mr Trevelyn, you have won. In thirty-
seven years I have never, ever, met such a determined and stubborn man.
I am prepared to allow my men to connect you to the national grid for one
reason only. I genuinely feel sorry for the saintly woman, your wife, still
with family in the house to care for. She indeed has a large cross to bear
with you around. Good day Sir." The inspector turned abruptly, walked
towards his men, gave instructions and left.

Very soon mains electricity lit up Regius Farm. As Trevelyn whistled
a happy tune he wandered back to the house, light of step, pondering the
anticipated meal. Before he could open the kitchen door, Iona cut off his
path. "I've won!" announced her husband. She then made a short telling
speech informing the farmer that due to his behaviour through the winter,
his stubborn determination to do battle with the Electricity Board had
created misery for the family. He was not welcome in the house that evening.
"What about the evening meal?" he asked. "Work it out for yourself within
the comfort of the hay barn. Good night you stubborn old man." And the
door slammed shut, then locked. Trevelyn discovered that night what is
was like to be a cat, sleeping in the hay barn; but content that he had won!

With mains water, sewerage and electricity, also came the municipal
dustman who took away rubbish that for centuries had been recycled, by
country people in particular. Finding other uses for items was a part of
life; it was expected and necessary, but a new generation just disposed of
unwanted things and turned their backs. The workhouse was sold off, a row

of almshouses too as Thurlchester Social Services Department absorbed homeless, poorer and widowed people into the city.

War time austerity gradually, very gradually receded. Food rationing stayed until 1955; building programmes were instigated; the City Council built houses with large gardens where the men folk were expected to grow the family's vegetable needs, while upon the farm Trevelyn constructed new buildings. The 'At cost' structures with giant cast concrete pillars and roof struts, corrugated asbestos roofing with breeze block internal divisions could house 100 pigs each. An economy of scale was being preached. New chemical fertilisers emerged that needed spreading. Prairie-style arable farming involving pulling up hedges, filling in ponds, felling 'inconvenient' copses of ancient woodland, took hold. A faster mechanised production of battery hens, large white turkeys, pigs in narrow pens, became popular. Industrialised farming with its consequential loss of intimate knowledge of animals was now in vogue.

In town and city an almost crazed mania for demolishing old buildings, narrow streets, ancient squares gripped the planners under the influence of a Swiss/French architect named Charles Le Corbusier; a Russian Soviet-style utilitarian appearance gradually dominated public and private buildings alike. Hospitals, schools, town halls, post offices, train stations all lost their character.

Out went the wrought iron balconies, Victorian gothic, Tudor beams and Queen Anne chimneys. In came straight lines, conformity, steel, glass, chipboard. Character was out, replaced by a dull functionality. Everything was equal, no building required the character enhancing respect of uniqueness or difference. Into the crass conformity stepped a new breed of entrepreneur or developer with an almost visceral hatred of nature in all of its forms. The countryside and farming was muddy; cover it with a slab of concrete; build roads of disproportionate size to enable travel all day, without actually going anywhere.

Rushing here and there those self important egocentric types tore down history, stripped away inherited culture, set aside custom and practice. A banal orgy of destruction under the twin banners of 'new' and 'modernisation' occurred. Their loathing of profession, codes of conduct people who studied for examination; the generosity that was born out of a devotion to the scriptures all eluded them. A semi-literate thuggish determination gripped them as they single-mindedly pursued money, then consumption of food and drink, paid for sex, Satanism as a creed, consumer durables, plus a plethora of gadgets with which to console themselves in their desperate inner unhappiness, boredom and loneliness. Unhappy due to spiritual emptiness and physical pain self induced by excess. Rene Descartes the famous philosopher had written in his work 'Meditations', "Cogito, ergo sum," (I think, therefore I am,) which needed amending to "Woolworths, ergo sum," in order to fit the prevailing circumstances now.

Britain had, in 1945 been the moral leader of the world. Alone in 1940 it held back the terrifying National Socialist tide, those hideous European dictators and their ilk; yet within a few years totalitarian concepts of governance were gripping many, the Church too fell silent as illiterate intellectuals with dubious intention gripped the conscientious. Into the vacuum stepped the greedy, backed all too often by strong arms.

Thurlchester, in common with too many other cities, succumbed. Its Lord Mayor, (of whatever persuasion), acquiesced. The council prevaricated; those in authority dithered and wrung their hands as a new breed of rascal; the spivs set aside convention, filled their own pockets, ideally without recourse to government's administrating taxation. The bribe was a legitimate currency to them.

An unpleasant young man from a tough street of inner Thurlchester emerged. Loathing authority, having managed to somehow evade military service, rumours circulated that he had stolen drugs from a doctor's surgery, taking them prior to a medical examination which concluded high blood pressure. Poor feet were noted, simply because he had wrapped them in damp rubber strips in order to destroy the upper layers of skin. Psychologically insecure, Les Feather sought only to advantage himself over his fellow man in his every dealing. He personally did the minimum, whilst extracting the maximum; if necessary using one of his retinue of camp followers.

Job-hopping from one menial position to another he was noticed selling Paraffin, using his gang to push the wooden transport that held a metal barrel containing the liquid. He never actually soiled his own soft pudgy hands, but developed a patter at the gate or within the doorway for selling the fuel whilst his rather surly mates delivered it. His style developed a menace to it, almost forcing women in particular to accept more than they needed for the week, thus enabling alternate weekly visits, giving him opportunity to carry on his trade around surrounding villages. The village forays gave Feather and company the opportunity to plunder crops from fields. His attitude being that farmers had too many brussels, cabbages, and carrots anyway. The plundered booty from his loathed farmers was offered as a side line upon the doorsteps of Thurlchester cottages.

Fed up with so much walking and general physical effort Feather spotted what he thought was another opportunity to advantage himself. Needing absolutely no qualifications, yet conferring a distorted form of respect upon the character, he would from now onwards wear a suit and tie. Les Feather became an estate agent. The ne'er-do- well gang of Sid Young, Dick Wise, and Willy Balls became something called 'negotiators'. They had one plan. To sell land and property quickly, circumventing every known convention of propriety, copyright, and manners in order to have as much spending money as possible. Their contempt for everything was manifest. A decent man would not even have employed them to clean his latrines. If they shook your hand, which they seemingly needed to force upon everyone with a regularity, it was subsequently advisable to count your fingers. Worship to them was a ritual played out in front of the shaving mirror each morning.

They came to the notice of Trevelyn one day when a neighbour called at the farm to ask why he was selling up and where were the family going. Flabbergasted by the question the farmer was immediately worried by the implication. His mortgage was paid up-to-date; so why should anyone question his permanence upon a farm that he had invested his life into and had a son committed to? The visitor explained that along the main road where much traffic passed there were 'For Sale' sign boards saying: 'Feather and Co.' Trevelyn and his wife visited the site of the boards, removing them and vowing to see a solicitor when they next visited Thurlchester for the market. It was, however a very disconcerting episode.

The visit to Henry Waddup proved less than helpful. He muttered platitudes such as: "Everyone has to make a living," or "That's life today." Clearly Waddup had no stomach for the issue. When they visited the bank, even the elderly and seemingly honourable Fore-Smith turned away from the obvious breach of protocol. Yet despite not being prepared to discuss Les Feather and Co., he did wish to pursue the issue of whether or not

Regius Farm was for sale, reminding the farmer of his mortgage obligation to the bank, and offering to provide a customer should he wish to sell. Trevelyn and his wife were cruelly stunned by the priorities and manner adopted. Life had indeed changed.

A majority of the veterinary requirements for the farm were handled by the couple; veterinary fees associated with a call out, their remoteness causing delays necessitated a stockman being self sufficient. This was quite usual for skilled owners and managers; it represented good husbandry.

Castration became a regular deed, especially with pigs. One day the veterinary surgeon arrived to attend to a cow with calving problems. Trevelyn and his wife agreed to assist in castrating a number of young pigs. Upon this occasion the surgeon had brought along a young female student. Having assisted with the cow which was saved, the young woman set about the task of castration. A zeal and enthusiasm for removing the parts gripped her. Her vigorousness of mission, wild glint within her eye with gritted mouth, determined muscular contortions of her face combined with a vocal stridency indicated the arrival of a new breed. The farmer and his staff found a reason to leave the barn. They had never met a female quite like this one before.

*   *   *

Edwin and Iona Trevelyn had enjoyed a fruitful marriage. Events took their natural course and the remaining four children each found mates. Wedding ceremonies took place until the time of the last one; Heather, to Francis. The farmer and his wife were also grandparents. Very quickly they found themselves with eight grandchildren, producing some very large family gatherings that dined well from the home produce. Then with in-laws, the McNiven clan, and visitors from Cornwall; 23 people might share a bank holiday together.

One day a letter arrived from Penzance. It was a plea to Uncle Edwin from Henry Provins, the son of Agnes, for advice and assistance. Leaving Edward in charge for a few days Edwin took the train to Cornwall and stayed with his sister; she and her family had always managed, but struggled. Despite fine soil, hard work and worshipping the Lord, life had caused them to graft. A request from London flower markets for fresh cut blooms had prompted them to invest in anemone growing. By cropping with the flower then harvesting using part time staff; boxing, transporting to Penzance Train Station for the journey to London, they satisfied an eager market which showed much potential for growth.

The younger man met his uncle from the train station and gave all appearances of wanting to cry. A rather quiet journey within the pony and trap took them from the town through several villages to the farm. Entering the property with the primary school upon their right just turning children out for a playtime break; their joyous squeals at encountering fresh air a pleasure to behold. They journeyed down a classic Cornish farm driveway, high walls either side with the occasional gap, where a gate hung from granite posts, the walls covered in moss grass; various hedge plants, both shrub and trees, flowers too, that had arrived courtesy of the wind and birds.

The shale and gravel hardcore drive twisted turned, rose up, then dipped; turning first right then at right angles to the left, all of the time having a grass ridge running along its centre. Then just as the visitor, or a stranger thought that he was going nowhere, the final turn left and down to reveal something so precious, the livelihood of a family for many years, an expression of that family's cultural identity; their hobbies; sport, working life and entire reason for existence all contained within a freehold. This special place in a beautiful part of the country was more than just a livelihood. It was a family farm.

The younger man wished quickly to explain to his uncle details of the plight that his sister and family found themselves in. He showed his relative the investment and infrastructure put into place. Now suddenly there was no market for the product. Prices had fallen to an extent that this particular small farm could not compete with. A multi-national enterprise had pushed them aside. Apparently the offending corporation specialized in employing retired bank managers, who without any recourse to ethics or loyalty to previous customers, were prepared to tip off the corporation with details of which farm might be in financial difficulties, or those who for whatever reason may be susceptible to an offer of cash for their freehold. They always paid less than the market price thus immediately showing an actual gain, whilst also writing off spurious investment against any profits. With bank managers and solicitors retaining intimate knowledge of everyone's financial affairs a number of local farming enterprises had been picked off, amalgamated, then turned into factory scale production.

Trevelyn asked about the company who were putting local people out of operation. Henry described a conglomerate known as Sporrow, run by a so-called charismatic Chief Executive, 'Chalky' White. However, their farming and horticulture side traded as Agri-Culture Ltd. The two men talked long into the night. Trevelyn drawing upon the words of the brilliant writer George Orwell said, "It's 'Big Brother'."

"And the holding company," replied Henry.

However they looked at it though the small producer was finished. With corporate lawyers, corrupt, biddable accountants and numerous opportunities to offset 'losses' Agri-Culture Ltd. were set to dominate anemone production in Cornwall. Henry's land would inevitably return to pasture, enabling more milking cows to be grazed.

Tragically for the small producer a multi-national company was more agile than even a sovereign national state in the tussle to advantage itself. Common policies within agriculture, between countries, then even a common legal system, gave to the corporate board room an unjustified edge. Even imperial preferences were being abandoned, which were of such great benefit to the British dominions and overseas territories. Our own people isolated; was Britain being wound up? A white paper had been published by the government which stated: "The British Government could not contemplate entering arrangements which would in principle make it impossible for the United Kingdom to treat imports from the Commonwealth at least as favourably as those from Europe." A sell-out of our families in Canada, Australia, New Zealand, South Africa, Rhodesia and the West Indies in particular, forced European products to be admitted into those countries with favourable terms.

The two men parted at Penzance Station, one lifting his bowler the other his cap. They shook hands but said little fully understanding one another's situation; a plight indeed. A generation separated them but the battle to farm independently, where nature and its cycles were respected, was being challenged. A 'Sword of Damacles' hung over their ilk. (Damacles, a 9th century BC legendary courtier of Dionysius, of Syracuse, Greece, similarly tested, was seated at a banquet beneath a sword suspended by a single hair.) Irrespective of wealth or circumstance the insecurity of human life was clearly demonstrated by events.

Trevelyn so thoroughly enjoyed his market day and consequential socialising that he had been a regular around Thurlchester since his marriage and farm purchase. Unexpectedly, one day he was approached by a so-called local 'worthy' with an invitation to attend the City Society, that philanthropic body which had been set up with a dowry from Lord Horace Abernethy. Monies generated by his success both within Britain and abroad in the sphere of agriculture were invested and had grown. The City Society had evolved as a provider of charity to the locality. The concept was sound. Until recent years genuinely virtuous men would meet once a month within City Hall, dine, then work upon projects to benefit their community. The December meeting involved suitable entertainment. It was the annual occasion for wives to attend during which a truncated Christian service was held, then following a meal perhaps music or other hospitable activities would be enjoyed.

Trevelyn joined, offering whatever facilities he had which might benefit the community. He felt only benevolence. The farmer quickly noticed however that only a very few members actually did anything. The Bishop, a headmaster of the Cathedral School, an engineer, and a chemist, all outsiders to the area in common with Trevelyn were particularly active. A central core of the organization was unfortunately former pupils of the Alienuns School who did precisely nothing except talk, albeit in a rather grand way and usually about themselves. They were apostates, enslaved by raw money power. At his first meeting Trevelyn was approached by a character who worked at the Alienums School. Phillip Ackroyd was a clerk or administrator, who had been a former pupil too. In other words he had never left school.

In a high-handed disapproving, snobbish and conceited manner he first looked the farmer up and down, curling his upper lip, and stated, "I do not remember you from the Alienuns School. Er, where was it that you were educated exactly?"

Stunned by the impudence, the outright arrogance, Trevelyn just murmured, "Not locally." Ackroyd then snapped, "Then you will do no good here, we are mostly old Alienuns." Trevelyn had provided him with everything he needed to know; the situation was summed up for Ackroyd and so he turned away, and back to his own group.

An old retainer, with a working life at the hall, Horace Teale saw and heard the affront; he was embarrassed, disgusted and very uneasy at what he had just witnessed. Teale knew of Trevelyn; that he was a man of philanthropic intent who had given various schools virtually unlimited access to his farm for geography field classes, history lessons and biology classes too. From the study of pond life up to higher mammals, generations of the Cathedral School and council schools, including Teale's own children, many had benefited from using the facility. Here was a man able and ready to give of what this world had bestowed upon him, who unlike so many present sought not medals, praise or selfish material benefit, but the ongoing knowledge that relevant good was being achieved.

Teale looked straight at Trevelyn and said, "Sir, it's disgusting. I'm sorry Sir, but ee made you look a right Charlie, Sir. Little do ee realise all you've done Sir. I'll tell people 'bout what ee said Sir." Trevelyn just sighed, then he said, "No, don't worry, but thank you."

Later that year the City Society changed again, with an influx of younger characters. Ronald Millett the sly, creepy sweet shop proprietor; Les Feather and Sid Young, estate agents, and their close friend Ashley Kavanagh the builder — a deviant, who enjoyed unnatural sexual practices including some said, with minors. They were particularly welcomed by the retired bank manager Fore-Smith who was now a consultant with Agri-Culture Ltd and a city councillor. Henry Waddup the solicitor, too, formed a tight grouping with them. Only Young and Feather were not formerly pupils of Alienuns School.

By the Christmas meeting Les Feather was dominating proceedings, with many others acting as little more than nodding donkeys to his command. As he spoke his head bobbed up and down in agreement with himself. Simultaneously leering, he said that salesmen should always smile; many were fooled but those who could judge character were not. "The coming man," declared one, "entrepreneurial," said another; "can turn a deal," muttered a colleague from behind a hand disguising his own features. He resembled the pigs from the description in 'Animal Farm' by George Orwell. Near the end of the story as they have taken over the farmhouse, they stuff ripened apples into their fat faces which drip with over-consumption and enjoy protection from the puppies that they had stolen at birth, turning them into guard dogs of extreme savagery. His staff played the role perfectly. Their hard faced women; fe-males, were culturally impoverished, caked with make-up and would jeer at outsiders, denigrating their every effort with a bitchy monotone.

The City Society owned the freehold; a terrace of early Georgian shops and offices which were fronted by a cobbled street. It had enormous character, an ambience unique within Thurlchester. Known as Cathedral Mews it benefited with extensive back yards, access to roads and an area of undeveloped land at the rear. Taken as a parcel, probably constituting 15 acres. Ron Millet and his mother traded from one of the shops and as the oldest leaseholder retained a little influence with the newer lessees.

Les Feather had became ever more vocal at Society meetings; his hustling, shuffling duck-like walking motion, combined with his size, ensured that he was noticed. A crude voice, localized accent, and disregard for the civilising convention of manners — he regarded them as a weakness — slapping backs, shaking hands, wanting to somehow acknowledge everyone and be acknowledged; he was clearly convinced by his own patter. Crudely he needed to continually drill, using his fingers, into every one of his body orifices. His nose, ears and backside evidently gave trouble, which needed attention, even in public. Having adjusted the front of his trousers, the hand bringing relief would be pushed at the next object or person of his opportunism. It was a case of "Hail fellow, well met." He did not like tweed or cavalry twill, those who wore it, and what they stood for.

Feather altered, even changed protocol to suit himself. Knowing no boundaries, self deprecation in others was exploited as weakness. The concept of tradesman, implying indentured apprenticeship with associated learning held no allure for him. The pride of trade, or profession with examination and a certificate was irrelevant. He traded in spiel. The armed services in particular emphasized this concept of progression. Feather and company needed sycophancy; the grovelling by men who should have known better was contemptuously accepted as the humiliation of yet another useful idiot.

The artisan with his unique pride in achievement was not even protected by the copyright laws when besieged by this particular gang. He was easy plunder, being unable to afford the relevant lawyers. At least he did not exhibit their low moral fibre though; he had standards. They indulged in satanistic practices of the occult to determine their way, the darkness showing through in their faces and condition of their bodies and minds. Their decadence born out of unheroic times had the allure of paganism, yet they would be unable to define that, as greed was all they knew, or sought. Feather was aggressively intrusive, yet a wimp, being frightened of blood. Quite insensitive to the past and other men's experiences having, along with his entire entourage, somehow evaded military service, together with the discipline and self-discipline resulting from such an experience.

Despite men in his present company having recently been tortured, wounded and even imprisoned, insensitively, he wore cheap Italian imported shoes with brass buckles or tassles, a shiny continental suit and already owned a car. He could only be described as an utter spiv.

At the Christmas meeting, Sarah his wife, a consumer, was plied by the fawning Millet with chocolates, or 'Mummy's comforts' as she referred to them. Sarah Feather claimed that she was unloved, not appreciated but was very important. She lapped up the sycophancy of the weak and vacillating shop keeper; when following the meal her podgy fingers pushed 'Mummy's comforts' into her mouth as she spoke. She was a vulgarian, cheap trash without modesty, who like her husband showed contempt for custom and practice. Talking during mealtime with their mouths full of food, spitting out bits as they did so, they stretched over anyone in order to reach the cruet or water. Stabbing at their plate of food, it was a case of 'me, myself and I'. These people came with demands. Now! All boundaries had gone.

Then a new Bishop was appointed, by promotion. He had previously served in London. Organising a Christmas concert involving a certain Miss Honnerine Oliphant singing both classical and sacred songs the bishop was not appreciated by Feather or his retinue. The atmosphere had changed, there was culture death. As the woman sang 'Nymphs and Shepherds come our Way' Sid Young broke wind, much to the amusement of his own wife, a sort of virgin strumpet in a leopard skin top and fishnet stockings, and the Feathers. A poltroon had indeed spoken.

Usually the sound of Young's voice was just like a castrati, (castrated males singing alto in church choirs during 17th and 18th century Italy) — a scraping high pitched rasp, as though somehow he was still in puberty.

Bishop Kendrick spoke with Trevelyn and his wife; evidently something about Feather was familiar to him, a memory was triggered, yet he was new to Thurlchester and this group. Strangers as yet, though some present gave to him concerns that he expressed with subtlety.

The City Society meeting had clearly been fixed prior to that evening. Feather, Young, Kavanagh, Ackroyd, Waddup and Fore-Smith amongst others, proposed the demolition of Cathedral Mews along with the wrought iron work and décor of the street, in favour of a flat-fronted glass and concrete structure towering four storeys, with a car park, amusement arcade and 10-pin bowling alley at one end. One person who was present and affected by the project was Ronald Millet. The craven counter jumper spoke glowingly of the plans; ironically, because it would see his shop demolished. He assured the committee that by replacing the Georgian structure a resulting larger premises would benefit all. His performance greatly pleased Feather who picked up on various of his points.

Very quickly Feather moved the gathering towards a vote which would commit the City Society to recommending its decision to the City Council. A positive vote would be binding. The Bishop spoke emphatically against it, as did a headmaster.

Trevelyn complained that inheritance, culture, posterity and good taste were being challenged. The spiv was annoyed by this, his plans were made, what he defined as 'progress, new and modern' must prevail. Eventually that evening's chairman, a rotating officer, called for a vote. It went in favour of demolition with redevelopment of the site. Having won in principle Feather moved quickly to secure his position. Kavanagh and others presented a set of pre-drawn plans that his firm would seek to build. Millett would liaise with all of the other leaseholders to alleviate concerns regarding the future. Sid Young's family were involved with demolition. Once the City Council ratified the Society's decisions, work could start; meanwhile the rear yards and other land would be prepared.

All of those in favour now began rushing around being incredibly important, their knees flicking as they strutted about, demanding urgent words with one another. Earnest words whispered into his ear appealed to Ron Millet; he liked the closeness, his only chance of intimate human contact; it warmed him especially when Ackroyd was close. The City Society had reached its nadir. Fore-Smith and Waddup assured everyone that the ensuing City Council planning meeting would back the decision taken by the City Society. Little more than a formality in fact. Work may well commence within three months. The coup de grace was delivered by Feather, who along with the offices of Henry Waddup the solicitor and Fore-Smith, would finance the entire project. Feather himself was to oversee the necessary reconstruction of leases, organize contractors, buy in services; in all but name became the site agent and financial controller.

Ron Millet had worked himself into a lather of excitement, as though an estate agent on heat; raising grovelling to almost an art form. What he perceived as his close relationship with Feather would now pay dividends. He resolved to visit the estate agent's office in the morning with a choice of his favourite sweets, together with chocolates for his wife, believing that was how businessmen did their deals. Never mind that Feather was not an old Alienuns or his unpleasant natural crudity; the man sent his children to the school, they were attending the Stultus, a sort of remedial class. In Millet's day Stultus children were ridiculed, but not now.

Les Feather patronised the school, liked to discuss school, indeed whenever he was asked about his own schooling he always changed the subject to the Alienuns, thus giving an impression that he sought to create his own attendance there. How the inverted snobbery of the 'nouveau riche' breeds and distributes insecurity. Two distinct groups of people left the City Hall that December evening, those who wished to flatten the architectural heritage of Thurlchester and those who favoured traditional buildings of the appropriate scale. It was as though they were from two different countries. False bonhomie had won the evening though. A cleansing of the Augian Stables, (to borrow from the tasks of Hercules written within Greek mythology) was now, long overdue.

Trevelyn and his wife liked to walk their land and talk. The afternoon following the City Society Christmas function, before milking and during Iona's poultry round they left the house together, dropping off bones left over from the Sunday joint of lamb for the cats, who pounced upon the remains then happily began licking, gnawing and growling. Once into the fields the couple began discussing the previous evening. Their conversation concerned developments, attitudes, people's actual intentions. Trevelyn resolved to immediately leave the City Society. That deep, often misunderstood emotion disappointment, had taken hold. The farmer used his penknife to dig up thistles, cowslip roots and various unwanted species, as they talked about life.

A harsh attitude was affecting people, churches left unlocked during the 1930's depression when people were actually hungry had to be kept locked now. A despotism and authoritarian attitude overcame the new breed of bureaucrat. The tyranny of psychological oppression. George Orwell had written about 'Big Brother'. Crime levels were increasing, murder, an accepted everyday occurrence, had reduced the value of life by cheapening its sanctity, yet a form of abolition of private life, of statism gripped political thinking. British people, unlike continental Europeans, had revelled in communal activity which was not official, or part of the state. Hobbies, societies, clubs, organised sports both individual and team games were part of the British heritage and invention. The country's love of gardens and flowers with small scale agricultural enterprise was intuitive. In 1940 the feeling of 'We are all in it together' was exemplified by the home guard.

Incredibly, the country had during Trevelyn's adult life twice survived the Europeans' intoxicated blind loyalty to party, power, corrupted thought using a certain style of perverted language and ideas that bred conformity. Yet the attitude of some within the City Society, let alone Greater Britain, now reflected a harshness more associated with republican Europe.

A conference held in Berlin had actually discussed: 'How will Germany dominate the peace after it loses the war'. Held in 1944; the French collaborative government of Marshall Petain and Pierre Lavel, based in Vichy, were understood to be present. Now within so-called peacetime 'The Treaty of Elysee' was signed by Konrad Adenauer the leader of West Germany, and Charles de Gaulle, President of France. Ratified, or re-signed, upon the High Altar of Reims Cathedral, (the debauched usage of a holy place if ever there was one), it agreed that the two nations would always agree an agenda and mutual self interest for the European Economic Community meetings previously designed by Dr Wather Funk and the Führer; of a recent German government. It all bore a frightening resemblance to the now Soviet Russian controlled eastern German Zone; under its leader Walter Ulbricht. That none of their so-called partner nations would ever be able to prevent their onward march was secured by treaty law.

Trevelyn and his wife were very sad. They had made terrible sacrifice, experienced bad things, paid their dues and here again just as their farm was paid off, they had an asset to be proud of, the fruit of sheer hard work, tenacity and worry, to pass on to their own children, with grandchildren in the wings, then their own Conservative Party Prime Minister Harold Macmillan proposed joining the creature born out of Adolf Hitler's nightmare visions for German living space; or 'Lebensraum'. They could not see their way clear now if their own country were to capitulate everything to treaty law, indeed a consent to conquest, when two wars had failed to destroy the greatest democracy since Great Helens. Perhaps only emigration was left for an upcoming generation.

As they walked back along a footpath, who should cross their path but old Joe Pruden, village character, veteran of the great war, a countryman who sadly never accumulated the necessary capital to buy a farm, but developed his part-time holding upon a couple of acres. Joe was a lineman, responsible for the maintenance of a length of road, gullies, ditches, and water channels working for the Council. He suffered terribly with war memory nightmares that were sadly best dealt with by consuming copious quantities of ale, known as 'benders'!

Unfortunately his drunkenness often caused an embarrassed son to wheel a barrow to the Eaton Alms, smack him semi-unconscious, place him into the barrow then wheel it homeward. If he drank excessively in Thurlchester or a nearby village Pruden's half-shire horse would trot him home without even a command. Once the village policeman tried to assist when Joe dropped his cigarette, unable to pick it up; the constable retrieved it, handing the item to the drunken man. Joe then brushed it and the policeman away saying, "I want my own cigarette, not your bloody cigarette." There were many stories circulating regarding Joe Pruden getting home at night.

He stopped Trevelyn and Iona, wanting to discuss politics; chewing the cud over current affairs was usual if you passed him along the way. Upon this occasion he was very concerned about the ongoing existence of his beloved smallholding. It meant everything to Joe. Four milking cows, two or three pigs, geese and hens, all bought from Trevelyn. Not only did it occupy his mind but the income provided an annual holiday, together with certain luxuries that his Council wage could never sustain. Above all it was part of his culture; a countryman relaxed with his natural lifestyle, happy with his lot, having served his country; a small compensation. The three people entered into a very serious philosophical discussion.

Earlier that week Pruden had read the newspapers, listened to the radio, and became horrified by the intention of the British Prime Minister Harold Macmillan to seek membership of the European Economic Community, promulgated by Adolf Hitler's government. Little more than the German plan to control the political, economic, judicial and military governance of Europe. The civil and economic part dove-tailing with the German military commander Reinhard Heydrich's book concerning the military suppression of Europe. It would regulate out of existence his own smallholding, aside from the man's family; the pride and joy of his life.

Then only the previous day in Thurlchester, the Conservative and Unionist Party had introduced in public their candidate for the constituency at the next general election, whenever it occurred. Previous representatives, the retiring incumbent included had a considerable knowledge of agriculture. Only a man fully understanding the needs and problems of the land, food production, conservation, together with country ways and aspirations could fully claim to represent the area.

Incredibly the Conservatives paraded a character described as doing 'something in the city,' meaning London. The mystique surrounding him was odd; why could they not be honest about exactly what he did and how he earned his money? His diction was foreign to Thurlchester, his chinless flaccid look, soft podgy hands and rather immature giggly approach suggested a gilded background. What however concerned Joe Pruden was the man's clear obsession with supra-national structures, big business, state control and signing up with European Government; the system evidently preferred by his party leader, Mr Harold Macmillan. Joe asked Trevelyn his thoughts; where would Regius Farm stand with the proposed new regime? Both Trevelyn and his wife were horrified and quite disgusted with the news. As a veteran of the great war too, having lost a son, together with several other family members due to the recent war, one family member held as a prisoner of war, tortured; where was the thanks from the State? The Conservative and Unionist Party had always emphasised patriotism, the union of Britain — which formed part of their name; law and order, Queen or King and country, duty, and the Church. They accepted monies from the farming community in return for sensitive reform, respect for the unique problems of tussling with the elements of nature to keep a nation fed. Here, they were planning to replace liberty with authority, a tyranny of unelected who would drain the spirit of a nation, whilst regulating out of existence small scale enterprise.

It was John Stuart Mill who stated the right of a man to "freely shape one's life as one wishes." Then the philosopher Isaiah Berlin had noted: "Few governments, it has been observed, have found much difficulty in causing their subjects to generate any will that the governments wanted." Despite the moral strength of the now retired Winston Churchill who warned: "We are with Europe but not of it. We are linked but not compromised. We are interested and associated but not absorbed. We do not intend to be merged in a European federal system."

There was an all pervading loss of collective confidence permeating the governing class. It seemed that two world wars, relative weakness of the pound sterling to the American dollar, then the mess generated by the so-called Suez Crisis had all taken its toll. The labour unions were virulent and gaining power. Traditional authority, that radiated decency, the school master or mistress, the clergyman, and doctor were now challenged. Trendy thinking sowed doubt and confusion regarding safe British institutions; as the cement of society dissolved people were being rendered feeble and disorderly. Indeed no country is secure without its own traditions, beliefs and myths, but people had forgotten so quickly and easily, perhaps due to prosperity.

Those whose philosophy had been vindicated despite personal sacrifice were the people who persisted their belief in British custom and practice, the British Crown and constitutional monarchy, Parliament, and our right to evolve our own laws. Never more so than in the 1930's as European dictators, some wearing armbands upon the left, others on the right sought a mind-numbing conformity through violence, intimidation and stylized language. Trevelyn and his wife had seen it, experienced it and yet believed that duty with sacrifice was sufficient to ensure their survival, they trusted that politicians would do the rest. As they bade farewell to Joe Pruden that evening, it was with a heavy heart. Perhaps an ultimate position of liberal thought and practice had overcome the country.

The questioning of everything rendered Britain and her people unable to define, or to defend themselves.

* * *

The City Society of Thurlchester had achieved the majority's aim of demolishing Cathedral Mews, Les Feather and his cohorts were triumphant. Trevelyn and certain 'outsiders' had left. Upon market days Feather could be seen spivving around the periphery of the market activity. Not too close so as to dirty his imported shoes or splash his shiny suit, but there were backs to slap, hands to pump, well rehearsed, tired old clichés to spout; above all some eyes to avoid. "I can sell anything," was his refrain. "Yes," interjected a wizened old countryman, leaning upon a cattle pen, "we remember poor old granny." He paused for effect. "Dreadful business," he spat out in a deep voice.

The comment implying the sale of his old granny for profit bounced off Feather. He invoked a champagne lifestyle for all as he approached farmers to buy something he pathetically called 'new land'. There was no such thing. Trevelyn always rebutted the advance by explaining that he had no desire to sell his own job; who would?

The rhythms of nature were unknown to Feather, indeed his excess even disturbed the proper ordained rhythms of this body. Now a grotesque caricature of an 18th century dandy; physically and egoistically puffed up; he had debauched both his soul and person. When he sat down the bulge of his paunch extended over his knees. The invisible trouser belt created a lower protuberance; the shape of his legs had gone. Gulping as though a fish for air, his chin wobbled as he waffled platitudes. He was incarcerated together with his wife, within a prison of materialism. Their ignorance, lacking intellectual curiosity, loathing of music, literature, art, indeed any cultural activity, was openly paraded, creating a passive obedience amongst all followers whose divinity of objects, trinkets and consumer durables too, formed part of the bond. It dominated their conversation of one-up-manship. A stale bland chatter of tittle tattle doing the umpteenth round of the year sustained them.

The acquiescence of so many to demolish Cathedral Mews was quickly followed by development. Feather had no time to wait, very large sums of money were changing hands. A nationally known shop chain signed a lease to rent the biggest unit, as did a leisure company for the bowling alley, and car parking franchise too. Feather placed his own home upon the market at this time too, generating many jokes in good and bad taste concerning his intentions. Evidently Mrs Feather needed more space.

Units were leased, the project neared its end as Millet the sweet shop proprietor realised that there was no room for him.

Disbelieving, he visited a public house for a few hours before plucking up sufficient courage to confront Les Feather, within his own premises. Feather sneered at the craven wimp, then produced a tirade of verbal abuse and filth directed at the sycophant who bit his knuckles then began to cry as he wet himself. He was literally pushed out of the property leaving a trail of urine, as foul abuse was hurled at him. Despite being an odious creep Millet genuinely believed that he had a friendship with Feather. Never having travelled, unread, he had little capacity for clear assessment though. The bully had used him as Mr.V.I. Lenin of the Soviet Union had used the Social Democrats and other fair minded people. As 'useful idiots'.

The following morning after milking and breakfast Trevelyn took his tractor with its box loaded with new posts and wire far over his fields in order to mend a fence; 'Mickey' the old sheep dog accompanied him. They were to work alongside Assers Brook. The dog jumped out with glee; a less familiar part of the land offered adventure for him.

Presently, as the farmer worked the dog began to make an incredible fuss, barking, running to and fro. Trevelyn decided to wander over and investigate. There, lying face down in the brook was a male body. Closer inspection showed that it was none other than Ronald Millet. Nearby on the river bank was an empty whisky bottle, a large empty container of aspirins, and folded plans showing the Cathedral Mews development. Millet was cold and stiff from rigor mortis. Trevelyn remembered that he had last seen the hapless creature ahead of himself within a city bank. Unaware of who was behind him, Millet was boasting to a bored elderly couple of his acquaintance, perhaps customers, regarding all of his important work carried out in connection with The City Society. He gave such an impression of his role, name dropping, as he clutched his case under one arm with a stance often taken by academics. Rolling up and down on the balls of his feet, chin airborne, eyes fixed upon infinity he made pathetic claims as to his own importance.

Any person who had experience beyond a few streets of Thurlchester, or was not bigoted through the self deluding parochial belief systems of the Alienuns School former pupils could see through Millett. He and his ilk chasing medals and praise, the approval and nod from those whom he deemed important, a chance to be seen talking especially in public with certain people; an opportunity to slight those whom he despised for no reason, and how they did slight outsiders, usually because they saw them as a threat. Their depth, intelligence, travel and knowledge easily exposed the Millets of this world, showing just how parochial and shallow they really were.

At City Society meetings certain abuse of and social humiliation to outsiders, was for example enacted by not responding when an outsider spoke. Changing the subject if an outsider tried to make a point, of sniggering or simply talking past them. Either way, only the narrow clique were ever given a proper hearing. Just as within a totalitarian society, where all but a few were an audience to the self appointed. They actually destroyed civil society and philanthropy by clogging up the natural flow of human discourse. Outsiders were sent to a sort of psychological and mental Gulag until they approved whatever the clique was desirous of.

Never mind that Feather, Young, Padget Kavanagh et al ate in the street, eschewed reverence, the concept of duty, valour, sneered at spiritual practice and intellectual property, were sexually filthy, even illegal, the nouveau riche had arrived — with all of its vulgarity and coarseness but lacking the accepted checks and balances that had earlier stabilised social activity.

Ron Millet had tried to ride a particular stream, was always out of his depth, then inevitably paid the price. The absence of virtually everyone known to him at his funeral spoke volumes. Contempt, expressed by silence, can be withering.

Trevelyn had left the City Society, unable to tolerate the motives of so many. Not though before the Bishop of Thurlchester had recalled his earlier memory of Les Feather who he sometimes referred to as the 'Blow Fly'. The Bishop had served a parish in East London, where a woman's refuge accepted many prostitutes into its care, often following time spent in hospital. Some of the ladies' customers were by nature, violent towards women.

The grasper Feather, with perverse carnal desires, essentially a nitwit in a suit, was known to travel to London every few months, occasionally with his acolytes. Stating that the couple of days absence as being necessary due to very important work needing to be carried out in the property world. How an unqualified spiv would be needed was never explained though. He was adept at building quite a story, always emphasising his own importance. The Bishop eventually worked out that it was none other than Les Feather who treated his paid sexual partners with abhorrence, having briefly huffed and puffed his lot. Stories abounded in the parish that fitted the character of Feather; accordingly the cleric quietly stood down from the City Society, by citing other pressing committee work needing urgent attention. Not a hard professional churchman; he brought love with gentleness, derived only from the Holy Bible itself, and the apostle Paul it was however unwelcome within this environment. The philanthropists gradually faded away, using this or that excuse.

Euphemisms, that were in fact transparent, allowed the charity-minded type a way out. People who wished to work for others and the good of the community found outlets which did not enrich bullies. Those climbing socially with the loudest voice, combined with a disregard for convention were left to feed off one another, like cannibals. The phrase 'social changes' perhaps underestimated the proliferation of greed enjoyed by being of, rather than outside, the right clique. Lord Horace Abernethy was almost certainly turning in his grave as people who he would never even associate with, let alone share their company at a dining table, now controlled his dowry. Their affectation in all matters appeared to sell them to a gullible populace who failed to discern sycophancy or motive.

Then, quite suddenly, as Cathedral Mews was completed, Les Feather realised his assets. The sale of his private house combined with a staff buyout of the estate agency allowed Feather to leave rather abruptly for Spain and its sunny coastlines. A country that did not have an extradition treaty with Britain offered a safe haven for many a hustler. Les and Sarah Feather joined their ranks with some ease, and his estate agency, which became known as Wise, Young, Balls. Dick, Sid and Willy evolving as joint proprietors, displayed, in the crudest form the planners would allow, their services.

Meanwhile, Cathedral Mews required urgent remedial work carrying out to its structure which rapidly obeyed the laws of gravity, by sinking into an ancient water course. Evidently, unseen works below ground level had not been carried out despite inspection by a former drinking friend of Les Feather and Building Control Officer Mark Spencer, who quickly resigned from the local authority, emerging as an assistant to Sid Young. Several insurance companies were required to pay for extensive work upon the Mews initially to make if safe, then subsequently to finish it to the required standard. However, it started to crumble during its first winter. The mortar had not been mixed to a proper strength, given its load bearing requirements and natural climatic conditions.

The difference between the estimated costs of the Mews and the actual costs were in Spain with Les Feather. He not only enriched himself and his pension fund, the scam also provided a lump sum for him to involve himself in the now burgeoning property and tourist industry of the Costas. With Spain and General Franco encouraging investment from any crook who chose to move to the sun, his future and protection were guaranteed.

* * *

Walking through Thurlchester one day after a stock market Trevelyn paused and spoke with an ageing man sitting upon a blanket selling matches, pipe cleaners and pegs. Old Abe Travers had worked that spot since 1920, and leaving hospital. He had lost both of his legs in the Great War and suffered a certain amount of shell shock too. Eking out an existence he made just sufficient to feed himself. Family members brought him into the city using an old perambulator, lifted him onto the pavement for his shift, and collected him late in the afternoon. The farmer talked with Abe, who asked for little, despite being dealt a very poor hand in life. He was the last surviving character of the war in Thurlchester who casually sold merchandise thus. Now a dying breed countrywide, he and others appeared all too often as an embarrassment to the new generation.

Trevelyn had bought a packet of ten Players Weights cigarettes, dropped them by the old soldier's hand and talked with the man who so starkly contrasted with Feather, Young, Padget, Balls, Fore-Smith, Waddup, et al. Their grasping and selfish attitude to life compared unfavourably with that of Travers, who always expressed patriotic thought. The farmer pondered as he left the disfigured man, as to why those with so little would instinctively voice a love of the country, understanding their own freedoms; yet those who had so much complained unendingly effecting to know of better. Trevelyn decided to visit the Market Tavern, before the homeward journey.

The national mood had changed, quite noticeably. Public houses change too, in atmosphere, with the time of day. Lunchtime: businesslike, brisk, very temporary. After work day hours: a quick drink, an appetiser, social pleasantry. Then finally, the committed drinkers. As he entered, a sign was being posted, inviting attendance to local events. An alternative sort of female, a kind of yin yang tweaker was offering therapy for all manner of ailments, perhaps real and imagined problems, from the public rooms above the bar. Expensive therapy was becoming popular as previously unknown problems evidently affected so many. There was now mass communication, yet people failed to communicate; consequently their lives broke down. Another evening's entertainment involved various artists playing folk music; one, a sort of mystic Celtic warbler attended regularly; another sang compositions by a certain Bob Dylan who according to some, provided all of the necessary answers to life.

"The times they are a-changing," as Mr Alistair Cooke quoted from the popular folk singer during one of his weekly broadcasts on radio. Evidently President Kennedy of America requested through one of his speeches: "Ask not what your country can do for you, but ask what you can do for your country." He mentioned the folk singer Bob Dylan by name, as a generation were evidently listening to him, not to their elders. Kennedy's speeches raised the spectre of disharmony. Trevelyn's grandson Angus had questioned his elders regarding Mr Dylan and his proposed changes.

Protesting about the very freedoms that allowed the population to protest about issues in the first place seemed odd. Destruction of the free speech and the free spirit that drove democracies without state persecution was seemingly enunciated by the communist Woody Guthrie. His adherants, especially within the New York folk scene — Pete Seger, Julie Felix and Joan Baez — sang against the free West, evidently favouring the pitiless and godless Marxist societies. "We shall overcome." But what? Perhaps freedom itself? as they claimed to have history upon their side. A specious argument inviting laissez-faire attitudes to our traditions and value systems besmirching national sovereignty in favour of internationalism.

A line of least resistance was promulgated, interspersed between a strum upon a guitar or banjo, and a joint of marijuana.

Greenwich village was not completely different to Thurlchester, philosophically. The crowing rooster was unheard in New York City, yet the crowing of the chattering classes, the fickle Judas characters oozing a puss of unctuous charm with smarm, promoting those masters of war in the Soviet Union who were giving birth to terrorist movements worldwide, were in vogue. Whilst destroying spiritual practice and encouraging people to think the previously unthinkable through art, architecture, writing, and music, they were gaining credibility and credence.

Prime Minister Harold Macmillan had evidently lost his nerve as he sought acquiescence to old Europe and its crazy politics by surrendering British sovereignty. Further he gave plausibility to the closed society that was the Soviet Union by asking if their claim to need to imprison their people was as they stated, a desire and need to protect themselves and their revolution from the democracies.

As Trevelyn sank his pint before returning to Eatonville he mused that both the British state as indeed the American state would be destined to turn against its patriotic subjects. Prosperity with materialism had dulled a generation's senses, as children were, yes, actually 'beyond their parent's command' as Mr Dylan sang. Trevelyn saw within his adopted city a microcosm of the Western world actually unaware of why it was free, now unable to define itself.

Riding home he thought of Winston Churchill who had suffered terribly after the Second World War with a sense of dread and failure, because no sooner had two ghastly European dictators been successfully vanquished, along came another, even worse than the first ones, to create a terrifying empire protected by an 'Iron Curtain'. For this he had given a son. Now for those left however, there was much to do; it was harvest time again.

*　　*　　*

Extra labour had been hired, sons-in-law Francis and Gerard had taken annual leave; the children had returned from their summer's lease of Cornwall, full of anecdote, memory, and tales. Riding horses around Trezion Farm; ringing the bells within Truro Cathedral, seeing a snake called an Adder; putting on musical concerts, and reciting verse for the adults during summer evenings. Indeed a fascinating array of characters, some of acquaintance others part of the greater family, who in their own, perhaps unknown way, were destined to contribute to the children's upbringing and overall happiness then, and later in life.

For the several weeks of harvest sleep rarely seemed to matter. Early morning milking, then preparation of machinery before the dew had dried allowing cutting of wheat, barley, rye and oats, and a possible second cutting of hay then storage of straw for bedding. Hay and other feedstuffs were for the winter consumption by the stock. Iona brought lunches into the fields; flasks of tea, and homemade juices to drink. Tea was followed by pitchers of beer. By nightfall a physical exhaustion occurred like no other, as thanks were given for yet another fine day.

The dog played around all of the activity, and cats watched from the headlands as another field mouse or vole ran for its life. A 12-bore shotgun was kept handy to shoot rabbits who crept into the middle of the field until the last few square yards were left to cut, then they ran like — well, er, rabbits. Many would be destined for the cooking pots of Eatonville, some for the butchers' shops in Thurlchester, who paid cash for good young meat. City folk knew when to keep a steely eye peeled for the late summer extras.

Bottles were prepared for the retention of the autumn fruit, sealing jars that would re-emerge only after Christmas as the weather became colder. Villagers called by to collect berries and crab-apples from the hedgerows for brewing purposes. Last year's wine needed finishing quickly to release much needed bottles for the new product.

Then one evening, a Tuesday, bell ringing practice from 7:30 until the statutory finishing time of 9:00 p.m., provided an incident suitable for local tale. The ringers had always secreted away bottles of home-made hooch, 'larrup' some called it, others 'wobble water'. They took a nip after ringing a 'method' — it provided much needed sustenance apparently.

Unfortunately a character known as Joe 'Tenor' Bell wanted to off-load numerous full bottles of last years brew, in order to free his supply of bottles for the current year's harvest of berries. The ringers present decided to empty the bottles of varying flavours, which caused a weakening of their knees and legs, garrulous laughter and playfulness, unfortunately during an activity that required concentration. No one was able to apply their minds to the mathematical permutations as giggling replaced the calls of 'Bob' and 'Single'. A stay was broken, causing its bell to turn over and over before eventually coming to a natural rest. They lowered the remaining seven bells simultaneously in the manner of continental bell ringing, all clanging at once.

The din was heard across the fields, causing Trevelyn and family to cease their activity, listen to the racket and muse over what was going on. The vicar, along with a churchwarden, ran to the church whereupon they found 'Tenor' Bell and his band swinging upon the ropes of the downward bells laughing, mocking, cheering, as all decorum had vanished. The ensuing row would see Bell sacked as tower captain and many changes to the organization of local bell ringing practice. Several years would pass before either novices or experienced practitioners were trusted with church keys again. Some did not enter the consecrated property for months such was their embarrassment; a condition experienced by all human beings who are honest in their self appraisal.

With harvest now in, Iona organised a family party, before Guy Fawkes night and after harvest festival. Trevelyn was tired; it was not easy any longer to sustain the very long hours, but a family party would certainly relax him.

Everyone had arrived for the harvest party; kitchen and scullery work was finished, drinks were poured and circulated. The hubbub of over 20 people rose in decibels as the farmer was the last to join the throng. He began to speak, thanking all present for their efforts once again, the odd joke here, a memory there. His last sentence however silenced everyone, as he announced that it had been his last harvest. He stated that he would not live to see another harvest; his body could no longer sustain his will.

Iona chastised her husband for his morbid attitude; others too invoked positive images of the future; after all the farm was paid for and they were now a self sufficient unit. The future did indeed look bright. Politicians and climate excepted.

Three days after the party Trevelyn suffered a severe heart attack.

Dr Moffat, the general practitioner, sat down with Iona and read through his patient's notes. The former nurse actually knew what future her husband faced, given his medical history. The doctor told Iona to allow Trevelyn anything that he asked for. No whim or pleasure need be denied now. They both fully understood precisely what was coming. Later, when alone with her husband, she asked him if there was anything that he wanted, to which he immediately replied, "Yes, a fresh young rabbit casseroled with my favourite vegetables." He was quite precise. She then broke the awful news that Edward was in Thurlchester on business and no other man was available at that time of day to go and shoot a rabbit. The farmer just sighed, "Oh well," and left it at that.

He could hear the grandfather clock ticking downstairs, then chiming and striking. 'Tempus Fugit' was inscribed upon the clock. (Man who is born of woman has but a short time to live.) Yet he was not miserable, although there was a sadness because he would experience no more harvests or fattened turkeys. His sadness was for his country too, its demise, even despite honouring its treaty laws with Belgium and Poland, and now its likely break-up into Soviets of governed regions, all answerable to somewhere else in Europe. What would become of his style of agriculture drawn from 'The Georgics'?

Plato ran through his mind. The Greek had considered the nature of the state referring to the 'minimum state' that smallest possible unit that is able to supply the necessities of life. Like the Greeks, Trevelyn believed that British philosophical thinking needed to concentrate upon the minimum state. Surely agriculture and then defence of the nation state in its broadest terms would gain the highest considerations, for both in matters of arms and propaganda the state needed to defend and educate the population, if a way of life was to be preserved and ensure its continuance. Backed with a pastoral approach to agriculture a harmony between mankind, the animal kingdom and the land was an essential requirement.

He would, he believed leave a legacy for ensuing generations that were reminders of his philosophy, hopeful manifestations of his presence and achievements whilst in this world.

Somewhere a cockerel was crowing, no doubt regaling yet another success with one of his hens.

He thought about his various horses since childhood; he recalled hacking out along the bridleways, that was the best of fun. Of Autumn mornings with mist and cobweb; frosts followed by blue skies; the smells of putrifying humas within woodland and copse; of his dogs and cats over the years; his bulls and their success at county shows. Thinking of the evolution from Shire horses to machinery; sounds of clanking milking churns, pigs grunting and farting, poultry clucking and winter's still silence, he drifted into a restless sleep.

Iona went downstairs, very sad, unable to please the man who had given to her so much and shared with all, his culture. There was, however no one available to shoot a 12-bore shotgun, even if a rabbit consented to run in front of it. Walking through the kitchen she glanced through the lower glass pane of the back door and saw a line of cats just sitting there staring inwards. Like soldiers on guard, with the oldest puss Nimrod in the middle meowing. "Damn cats know that they cannot enter the house, why do they stare in like that?" muttered Iona. Nimrod then made a most unusual noise, catlike but not a call previously heard. It alerted Iona to open the door and shoo the animals away. She had too much upon her mind now to concern herself with cats.

Opening the door to the old warrior puss and his retinue of battered felines Iona glanced down; there in front of the cats lay a rabbit, quite dead. Disbelieving what she was seeing, Iona touched its fur. Still warm its neck broken, only killed a few minutes before by the cats, they delivered their quarry undamaged and laid it at the closest spot that they were allowed to the kitchen range. Iona looked at the rabbit, then at the cats who all looked straight into her eyes.

Slowly, very slowly the felines stood up, turned and walked away into the dull and murky Autumn afternoon. Nimrod was the last to leave walking almost in slow motion. Speechless, with tears in her eyes Iona took the rabbit to the scullery and prepared it for the casserole dish. Animals talk; they communicate in ways that humans may never understand, they have a highly developed sixth sense too.

The farmer was overwhelmed by this experience. Perhaps it was a 'thank you' from the cats for all of the fresh milk consumed, the initial pull from the cows teats as he cleansed the milk duct, or the bislings or beastings that is the early rich milk from the mother cow after a calf is born. Or maybe they just appreciated his company and being part of his farm.

* * *

The following day Trevelyn experienced another heart attack; a few hours later he died.

An Anglican funeral was arranged at Eatonville Church with a subsequent cremation. Josie Upcraft, the family's loyal retainer, prepared a fitting meal for the attendees. The coffin containing the mortal remains of the farmer was situated in the sitting room, open, for all to pay their last respects. Closed a few minutes before the assembled left for church, it was then transported upon the parish bier by the funeral directors' staff with the family walking solemnly in status order behind.

As it approached the church door, half muffled bells that had been ringing 1 through 8, 1 through 8, began to stand, or stop, treble first, as though reflecting the passing time of a man's life, until as the procession came to a gentle pause by the ancient carved wooden church door only the tenor bell solemnly rang; a full crisp note then a distant muffled one, then, nothing, it stopped too. A life was now to be celebrated. During the church service the words of the ancient Greek philosopher Calimachus were spoken to invoke a dying art, an ignored pleasure, that therapeutic pastime particularly relevant to the farmer; conversation. Calimachus heard the sad news of the death of his friend Heraclitus and within a poem known as 'Nightingales' expressed his feelings at the loss.

> *They told me, Heraclitus, they told me you were dead,*
> *They brought me bitter news to hear and bitter tears to*
> *shed.*
> *I wept as I remembered, how often you and I*
> *Had tired the sun with talking and sent him down the*
> *sky,*
> *And now that thou art lying, my dear old Carian guest,*
> *Still are they pleasant voices, thy nightingales, awake;*
> *For Death, he taketh all away, but them he cannot take.*

Then words usually attributed to the writer G.K.Chesterton were borrowed to emphasise the need for mankind to step aside from his selfish greed with a consequential imprisonment by false gods.

*When a man ceases to believe in God he does not believe
in nothing, he will believe in anything'.*

The world recently vacated by the farmer certainly now conformed to
Chesterton's observation. The eulogy contained the inspirational message
that in the end we actually remember not the words of our enemies but
in fact the silence of our friends. In prosperity our friends know us; yet in
adversity we know our friends.

Angus looked around the village church that had served a community
for nearly a millennium. He saw in its carvings, writings, art, and other
artistic expressions a culture, memories of wars commemoration of
battles; of myths and legends pertaining to a people who during their
amazing history did not just 'go with the flow'. A people who, long ago,
had floated stone down the river on barges then built themselves a village
and incorporated it into a country with its own unique laws, customs, and
practices. Since King Alfred the Great had begun an evolutionary process
to amalgamate a number of little kingdoms and even fiefdoms the most
enduring, safe and stable country ever known, around which a decent
system of agriculture ensured all were fed.

Angus could no longer see his grandfather, yet the man would remain
omnipresent. The farmer's mortal remains were subsequently cremated,
the ashes given to the widow. Various families then departed to Cornwall,
Nottinghamshire, London and where they had set up their own homes.

This left Iona to wander as she wished across the fields, in order to
scatter her husband's ashes. She instinctively knew where the right place
was, if there can ever be such a place. Walking from meadow to field, picking
up the line of Assers Brook, Iona thought about Edwin, and how one cannot
be wise and in love at the same time; perhaps that was why he dared to
leave his family's beloved Cornwall. Her mind raced, thinking about their
children and grandchildren, the two farms, his horses, the jokes, teasing
and tears. It was his politics and straightforward philosophy that defined
him, with a loathing of the unaccountable and unelected who seemed to
grab such power. The discernable arrogance of those who emerge from
the shadows to do their deed as Lady Macbeth , who, according to William
Shakespeare, did hers only to skulk away. His practical common sense,
decency, ambassadorial approach to farming, respect within the livestock

market place, with an undeviating kindness to animals and their kingdom, would be his lasting obituary.

He was quite simply of his time, which appeared to be passing. The farmer had never comprehended why agriculture was treated quite so shoddily by the 'here today and gone tomorrow' politicians. A long term strategic thinking with planning and practice was required to guarantee investment in, then success of, a country's food production. Those who worked the land were embraced during wartime, then all too readily discarded as the naval blockade receded. Imports and rhetoric were cheap. Iona remembered Edwin reciting 'Tommy', the poem by Rudyard Kipling, changing its meaning from the discarded unwanted military man to the local farmers' predicament. He lived through both experiences.

> For it's Tommy this, an' Tommy that,
>   an 'Chuck him out, the brute!'
> But it's 'Saviour of 'is country'
>   when the guns begin to shoot;
> An' its Tommy this, an' Tommy that,
>   an' anything you please;
> An' Tommy ain't a bloomin' fool,
>   you bet that Tommy sees!

And Trevelyn saw...

Iona remembered his complaint that individualism was increasingly a crime, that political ideas bred conformity, of how thought corrupts language, then language is used to corrupt future thought, giving a common purpose to ideologues. Indeed, 'Common Purpose' the neurological linguistic cult-styled brainwashing programme conceived by the European national socialist states, inspired through the purchase of the Frankfurt School in 1935 from the Soviet Union, used satanism, the occult, mental mapping coercion, political correctness, then subversion through networking; to cajole some into thinking that they were being given power.

They were both besotted and bedeviled. This was a considerable danger to any democratic society. How the fifth column worked hard for a post democratic era; people would just have to learn to live with less freedom thereafter. The loyalty of so many is then increasingly given to a political party, who gain power, only to be intoxicated by that power which goes on to abolish private life. People were then isolated by the state. Old Europe never learnt from its own history.

Trevelyn would look at his fellow men and invoke Pascal, the Frenchman who stated that the cause of all human misery was the inability to sit contentedly in a room. Unlike farmers, so many needed a supportive crowd, a clique around them, providing a bolster. Fighting the elements, providing nurture was another story. Her memory recalled him trotting the lanes with his pony and trap, of meeting with others who lived their equine culture.

She recalled how with stock puzzling occurrences may happen at any time, no matter how experienced you are, always expect the unexpected. His pride in the herd of cattle; how in hot humid weather the cows would gad – unexpectedly they would take off in a canter. His vocabulary might then change; the lead cow being re-christened as a hardened old bitch!

The widow found her spot, quite near to a pond and where the brook babbled, and no doubt had done so since before Assur himself. It created still places during its journey where watercress, kingcups and lilies grew, stickleback and frog co-existed, an elderly gnarled Spindleberry tree exhibited its red autumn fruit; willow and oak provided shade for a million gnats; the dragonfly briefly appeared, and spiders spun webs to ensnare their pray. The single- celled Paramecium and Chlamydomonas led their less complicated lives, whilst Trevelyn and his family had come to this place in the better weather to picnic or birthday party and play in peace, in communion with nature. The brook did not pause, as Iona undid the little cask. A still, murky autumn day, with harvest safely in and another farming cycle about to begin — without Edwin Trevelyn.

Iona held up the cask to spread her precious cargo upon their land and the water; as she did so a wind suddenly arose. Her hair and dress fluttered, the strong breeze caused her to turn as the tiny receptacle emptied its contents into the swirling air, which carried the ashes not to the ground but south-westward and sky borne.

They swirled as though a swarm of insects; leaving the woman, they travelled faster and faster away, becoming smaller in the afternoon murk; their direction unmistakably towards Cornwall, to Cornubia, that land of the saints; yes, back to Kernow.

Professor Arnold Toynbee, formerly Director of Studies, Royal Institute of International Affairs , Chatham House, London, wrote:

They were engaged in removing the instrument of sovereignty from the hands of the local national states, that they were, in fact doing with their hands what they were denying with their lips.

The author is aware of the following being a repetition:

"The broad mass of a nation will more easily fall victim to a big lie than a small one. The greater the lie, the greater the chance that it will be believed," stated Adolf Hitler, whose government conceived of the European Union.

Then in 1942 they expressed within a book written by the Reichsminister for the Economy — Europaische Wirtschaftsgemeinschaft by Dr. Walter Funk — plans that are now coming to fruition.

THE END

Or is it?

RECIPES

Fruit Crumble

Mix 4 ounces of flour, 2 ounces of butter or margarine, mix together by rubbing the fat into the flour, then add 2 ounces of sugar.

Place the chosen fruit or jam into a fireproof dish. Add cinnamon and cloves if it is an apple dish.

Bake in a moderate oven for up to one hour.

Shackels

Take the carcass of any fowl: duck; goose, chicken or turkey, hare, rabbit or other game. Break it up into a large saucepan or tureen. Add left over vegetables (not greens) and sauces from the roast.

Add fresh root vegetables as required, some water and stock. Simmer only until the fresh vegetables are ready. The remaining meat will fall off the bones.

Serve in soup dishes, with fresh bread. A very rich concoction

Cornish Pasty

Make short crust pastry. Roll out, sprinkle onto the pastry a mixture of small chunks of skirt beef, onion, turnip and potato. Add a knob of butter to assist creating gravy. Salt and pepper to taste. Keeping a flat bottom, fold over the pastry into a half moon shape. Press it up with your thumbs to seal it. If the pasty is eaten outside, create knobs of pastry upon each end with which to hold it whilst eating. Then throw the knobs away for the birds when you have finished.

If the dish is to be eaten within the home, and upon a plate, serve with fresh milk. Yes, really! Remember to make a hole in the top to release the steam before cooking. Cook for one hour, initially within a hot oven to bring the pastry up, later turning it down so as to properly cook the meat.

A proper Cornish Pasty contains chunks of meat; not mince, and no carrots, which are not a Cornish crop.

Beestings or Bislings
This is the first milk from a cow that has just calved. On the first day dilute
it by one half. Upon the next milking dilute it by one quarter. Add sugar
and salt. Bake as a milk pudding within a slow oven, or place it within a
pastry case, like an egg custard. Sprinkle nutmeg to suit.

Chowder (Lobster)

Cooking time   25 – 30 minutes
1 small pre-cooked lobster   1 pint water
1 – 2 rashers bacon
1 tsp finely chopped onion   1½ oz flout
1 medium potato, diced
½ pint milk or thick cream good pinch of sugar
salt, pepper
crisp toast fingers

Remove flesh from lobster, cut in small pieces and put aside. Put shell only
into pan with the water and simmer gently for about 15 minutes. Strain
and add enough water to make up to 1 pint again. After removing rind, cut
bacon into narrow strips. Put into a pan and fry lightly; add the onion and
flour and cook gently without colouring. Gradually add the lobster stock,
stirring all the time. When the sauce has come to the boil and thickened,
add lobster, cut into small pieces, and the rest of the ingredients. Either
reduce heat under pan to cook very gently or put in a double saucepan and
cook until it forms a thick creamy mixture. Serve with crisp fingers of
toast.

Serves 4

Taken from:
Every Day Cookbook – by Maguerite Patten, Hamlyn Publishers, 1960's.

Bibliography and Sources

A.K.Chesterton, *The New Unhappy Lords,* Candour Publishing.

Aristotle, *The Politics,* Guild Publishing

Athenon Ekdotike, *Greek Lands in History,* Ekdotike

Barton, *The Biblical World,* Routledge

Boethius, *The Consolation of Philosophy,* Folio

Bullock, *Hitler and Stalin,* B.C.A.

Cannon & Griffiths, *British Monarchy,* Guild

Daniel, *The Bible Story,* Grovesnor

De Burgh, *The Legacy of the Ancient World,* Macdonald & Evans

Fisher, *A History of Europe,* Arnold

George Orwell, *Novels,* Secker & Warburg

Herodutus, *The Histories,* W.Blackwood

Herodutus, *The Histories,* Wordsworth

Isaiah Berlin, *Freedom & its Betrayal,* Chatto & Windus

J.March, *Classical Mythology,* Cassell

Livingstone, *Greek Ideals and Modern Life*, Oxford Press

Macmillan, *Encyclopedia*, Macmillan

Niccolo Machiavelli, *The Prince*, Oxford University Press

Robert Burns, *Complete Works*, Lomand Books

Rudyard Kipling, *Complete Verse*, Hodder & Stroughton

Taswell & Langmead, *Constitutional History*, Sweet & Maxwell

The Good News Bible, Harper Collins,

Thucydides, *The Peloponnesian War*, Penguin

Virgil (C. Day Lewis), *The Georgics*, Jonathan Cape

Winston Churchill, *The Island Race*, Corgi

Zenothan, *Notes on the life of W. Blackwood*

Printed in the United Kingdom
by Lightning Source UK Ltd.
130614UK00001B/226/A